A*

GCSE

CHEMISTRY

THE MANCHESTER GRAMMAR SCHOOL

OXFORD

UNIVERSITY PRESS

OXFORD
UNIVERSITY PRESS

Great Clarendon Street, Oxford OX2 6DP

Oxford University Press is a department of the University of Oxford.
It furthers the University's objective of excellence in research, scholarship,
and education by publishing worldwide in

Oxford New York

Athens Auckland Bangkok Bogotá Buenos Aires Calcutta
Cape Town Chennai Dar es Salaam Delhi Florence Hong Kong Istanbul
Karachi Kuala Lumpur Madrid Melbourne Mexico City Mumbai
Nairobi Paris São Paulo Singapore Taipei Tokyo Toronto Warsaw
with associated companies in Berlin Ibadan

Oxford is a registered trade mark of Oxford University Press
in the UK and in certain other countries

British Library Cataloguing in Publication Data
Data available

ISBN 0 19 914741 8 (school edition)
     0 19 914749 3 (bookshop edition)

With thanks to Nick Rose, Lee Khvat, Jordan Mayo, Arunabha Ghosh, Adrian Turner, and Ronnie Davies

Typeset by Advance Typesetting Limited, Long Hanborough, Oxon
Printed in Great Britain

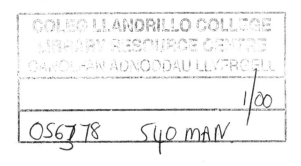

preface

The idea for the book which you are now reading came from a group of pupils at The Manchester Grammar School. Their year achieved what some league tables at least reckoned were the best GCSE grades in the country, yet they had found a dearth of good revision guides aimed specifically at able students. They thought they could do better, and the result (as part of the Young Enterprise Scheme) was the best-selling *Physics A* GCSE Revision Guide – written by the students for the students*. The rest, as they say, is history ... . The three Guides in this new series produced by the Oxford University Press are written by the same type of people who actually sit GCSEs – the candidates. They are wholly user-friendly, and we hope also that they are exciting in a way few other revision guides can achieve.

I hope you enjoy working with them as much as all of us here have enjoyed being involved in their production. Royalties from these books go to The Manchester Grammar School Foundation Bursary Fund, which pays for pupils whose parents have low incomes to attend the School; thank you for your help.

Dr Martin Stephen
High Master
Manchester Grammar School

contents

topic one

matter

Chemists use the word **matter** to refer to all substances which make up the universe. In fact, chemistry is the study of matter and how it behaves.

Matter can be in one of three **states** – solid, liquid or gas. The kinetic theory is used to explain how matter behaves.

The kinetic theory of matter

The kinetic theory (sometimes called the **particle model of matter**) states that all matter is made up of tiny particles, which are constantly moving, either freely or vibrating about a fixed point. The more energy these particles have, the faster they move.

Particles in a given substance attract one another. However, if they have enough energy, they can overcome these forces of attraction and break free. Usually, energy is supplied to particles in the form of heat.

Solids

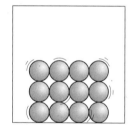

Particles in solids are strongly attracted and are not able to move around freely. They have a regular arrangement. They do, however, vibrate around a fixed spot. This means that the shape and volume cannot change.

Liquids

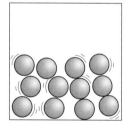

Particles in liquids have more energy than those in the solid state, so they are able to move over each other and flow to fill the bottom of a container. They do not have a regular arrangement. The shape of a liquid can change but its volume is fixed.

Gases

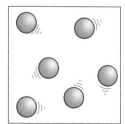

Particles in gases have enough energy to escape the attractive forces, so they are free to move in all directions at high speeds. The particles collide with each other frequently. They can expand to fill a container. Hence, the shape and volume of a gas can change. Since the particles in a gas are much further apart, they can be squashed into a smaller space (compressed).

Changes of state

Solids, liquids and gases can change state when energy is given to or taken from the particles.

Solid ⇔ liquid

If energy is supplied to a solid (usually as heat), the particles gain more energy and vibrate more violently. Eventually, if enough energy is supplied, they vibrate so violently that they can overcome the attractive forces and are free to move. This process is called **melting**. The temperature at which this occurs is the **melting point**.

Conversely, if a liquid is cooled, taking energy away from it, it **solidifies**.

Liquid ⇔ gas

Particles in a liquid are always moving around. Occasionally a particle on the surface gains enough energy to break free and escape, becoming a gas. This process is called **evaporation**. The higher the temperature of a liquid, the faster the particles move and therefore the more frequently a particle can break free.

If the temperature is high enough, bubbles of gas can form within the liquid and rise to the surface to escape. This is called **boiling** and the temperature at which this occurs is the **boiling point**.

> *(Note that a **gas** is sometimes defined as something that occurs naturally, at room temperature and pressure. You get a **vapour** when something liquid or solid at room temperature is heated in order for it to change to a gaseous state.)*

Below is a graph of a solid being heated. Notice that for pure substances, the melting and boiling points are sharp. For impure substances, the boiling point increases and the melting point decreases.

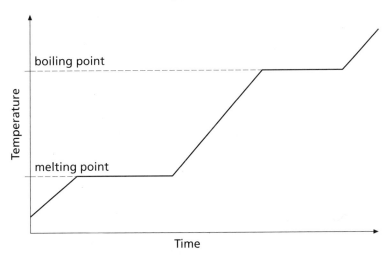

The effects of temperature on a pure substance

Summary

This diagram sums up what happens to particles during changes of state.

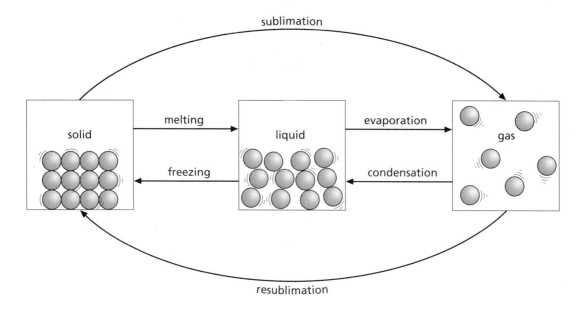

Notice the term sublimation in the diagram. Although most substances go from solid to liquid before evaporating, some skip the liquid stage and go straight to gas. Also, when cooled, the gas goes straight to solid. This process is called **sublimation**. Carbon dioxide sublimes, and solid carbon dioxide is sometimes called dry ice. Iodine also sublimes.

Evidence for the kinetic theory

Diffusion
Evidence for the existence of particles comes from experiments with **diffusion**, as shown in the diagram.

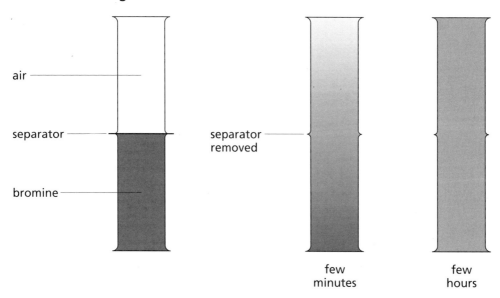

Demonstrating gas diffusion

Two gases, for example bromine (a brown gas) and air (colourless), are put in separate gas jars and one is placed on top of the other. After several hours, the gases mix and the mixture produced is a uniform pale brown colour. This shows that the gas particles are randomly moving around and eventually mix.

Note that diffusion also occurs when solids are **dissolved** in liquids, to form a solution (see p. 11). If one potassium manganate(VII) crystal is dropped into some water and left to dissolve, first the area around the crystal goes purple (the colour of potassium manganate solution). The purple colour spreads and eventually distributes itself through the liquid evenly.

Example questions

1.1 Label the melting point and boiling point on the following graph:

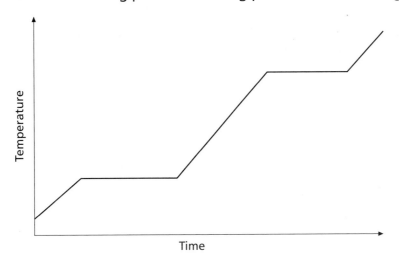

1.2 Why do gases take up more space than solids?

1.3 (a) Draw a labelled sketch graph of what happens when ice is heated from
        –5°C to 105°C.
     (b) On the same set of axes, do the same for impure ice.

elements, mixtures and compounds

More about matter

The world is made up of all sorts of matter. Chemistry is all about this matter, so it is useful to classify it according to its properties. In the same way that we can say whether matter is a solid, liquid or gas, we can also say whether it is an element, mixture or compound.

Elements

An **element** is a substance that contains all the same type of **atom**. It is the simplest form of a substance.

- Elements can exist as atoms (e.g. metals such as iron).
- Other elements can be made of several atoms of the same type joined together to form a molecule (e.g. non-metals such as sulphur).
- The **periodic table** lists all the elements, in order of increasing atomic number (see p. 99).

Mixtures

If you mix iron filings and sulphur, no chemical reaction occurs. You just end up with a **mixture** of iron and sulphur. You can **separate** the iron from the sulphur with a magnet.

- A mixture is a combination of substances which can easily be separated again by some means depending on the state of the mixture.
- The proportions of each substance in a mixture can easily be changed.
- No chemical reaction occurs, so no new substance is formed. There is usually no energy change (no heat is usually lost or made).
- Air is a mixture of gases; crude oil is a mixture of various organic substances (see p. 56).

Compounds

A **compound** is a chemical combination of two or more elements. If you now take the mixture of iron and sulphur and heat it, a new substance is formed. This is totally different from the iron and sulphur mixture. The colour is different and it is no longer magnetic. What we have is a compound. Also, if there was too much sulphur, the extra sulphur is left behind and does not react.

- Compounds have different properties from the elements of which they are made.
- The elements which make up compounds are in fixed proportions.
- A compound cannot be separated into its original components by physical methods, as with mixtures. Other chemical reactions or **electrolysis** must be used (see p. 66).
- Energy changes occur when compounds are formed. The reactants either get warm or take in heat to react.

More about mixtures

Solutions and suspensions

Some solids (**solutes**) dissolve in liquids (**solvents**) to form **solutions**. In effect, solutions are mixtures of the solute and solvent, although the solute particles break up and diffuse throughout the solvent. Concentrated solutions have more solute in a given amount of solvent. Solutions are clear (see-through, though they may be coloured).

Suspensions are mixtures of small particles of an insoluble solid in a liquid. They are not see-through.

Separating mixtures

Mixtures can be separated by various techniques, depending on the sort of mixture.

Filtration

Any liquid and insoluble solid mixture (suspension) can be separated using **filtration**. The liquid (filtrate) moves through the filter paper, but the solid particles (residue) are too large to do so, so remain behind.

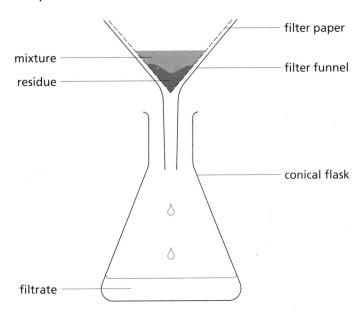

Simple filtration apparatus

Centrifugation

Instead of filtering, a **centrifuge** may be used to separate a suspension. A test tube with the mixture to be separated is spun around at a very high speed, throwing the solid particles to the bottom of the tube.

Decanting

A commonly overlooked method of separation is **decanting**. This involves pouring off a liquid. After centrifugation, with the solid at the bottom of the test tube, the liquid can be poured carefully off the top.

Two liquids that cannot be mixed (**immiscible**), such as oil and water, can also be separated by decanting. The oil floats on the top because it is less dense than the water. With care, it can be almost completely poured off into another container.

Separating funnel

Two immiscible liquids (such as oil and water) can be placed in a **separating funnel**, as shown in the diagram. The tap can be opened to let out the bottom liquid and closed again before the other liquid gets through.

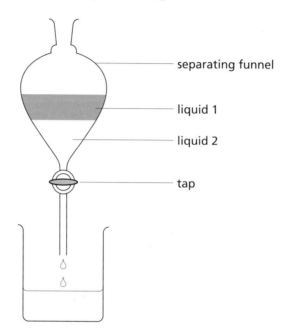

Separating immiscible liquids

Evaporation

When heated gently, the solvent from a solution can be boiled off. The solute is left behind as a solid.

Crystallisation

Since hot solutions can hold more solute than cold solutions, if you take a hot concentrated solution and cool it then some of the solute comes out of solution. It forms crystals which can be separated by filtration and drying.

Distillation

If you have a solution and want to obtain the solvent, you cannot use evaporation alone as the solvent boils off, never to be seen again. The vapour needs to be caught and condensed again. The apparatus shown in the diagram opposite can be used. The vapour condenses to a liquid (**distillate**) in the **Liebig condenser** and flows down the tube into a beaker.

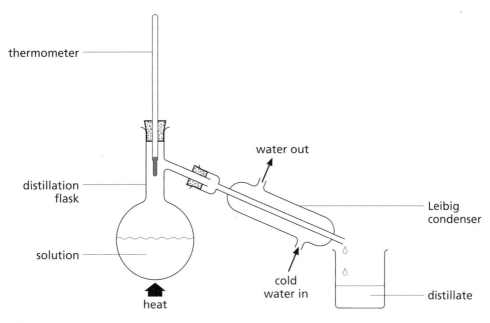

Simple distillation apparatus

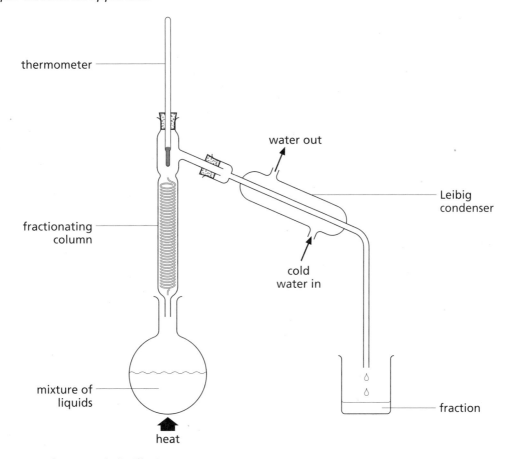

Laboratory fractional distillation apparatus

Fractional distillation

Different liquids usually have different boiling points. Separating a mixture of liquids by simple distillation can be difficult because the mixture boils over a range of temperatures, so the distillate will not be pure. In fractional distillation (or fractionation) the heated mixture passes through a fractionating column, which separates the vapours according to boiling point.

For example, if a mixture of ethanol and water is heated, the ethanol will start to boil at about 78°C. Any water vapour will condense out in the fractionating column, and flow back into the flask. The ethanol vapour rises to the top of the column, then is condensed and collected. After the ethanol has been removed from the mixture, the temperature in the column rises to 100°C and the water vapour is distilled.

Fractional distillation is used to separate crude oil into its fractions (see p. 57).

Chromatography

It is slightly more difficult to separate a mixture of different solutes. **Chromatography** is a technique that uses the fact that solutes of different mass and solubility are dissolved in a solvent and carried up a piece of chromatography paper at different rates. The solutes that are the most soluble move the fastest.

Chromatography can be used to separate a mixture of dyes, and to identify dyes in an unknown mixture.

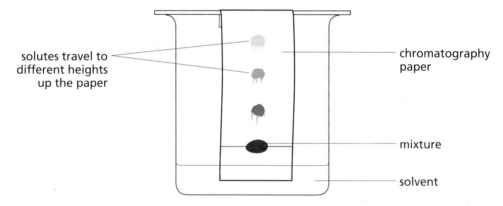

Simple chromatography apparatus

Example questions

2.1   Decide whether each of these substances is an element, mixture or compound:

(a) sodium chloride   (b) tin   (c) wood

2.2   Say how you would separate the following mixtures:

(a) salt and pepper
(b) oxygen from air
(c) liquid and solid parts of blood

2.3   Look at this chromatogram. What colour is sample X?

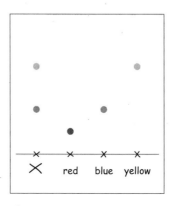

the periodic table

A brief history

The periodic table has been compiled over about the last century and a half. Before anything was known about electrons and how elements form compounds, early forms of the periodic table were devised by observing elements and classifying them according to their properties.

In 1863 Newlands realised that if the 63 known elements were put in order of **atomic mass**, their properties repeated in groups of eight. This was imaginatively called the **law of octaves**. Unfortunately this arrangement had several flaws, but it was, at least, a start in classifying the elements. A few years later Mendeléev arranged the elements by atomic mass *and* properties. He put similar elements in columns (down the page), leaving spaces for undiscovered ones. As new elements were found which fitted these gaps, this supported the idea of the periodic table.

The modern periodic table

The periodic table is arranged in order of atomic number (see p. 19), reading across the rows. The columns are called the **groups** and the rows are the **periods**. The section in the middle is the **transition metals**.

Group I metals are known as the **alkali metals**. Group II metals are the **alkaline earth metals**. Group VII are the **halogens** and group 0 (sometimes referred to as group VIII) are the **noble gases**.

Most elements are metals. Generally, non-metals are to the right of the table and metals are in the centre and to the left.

A summary of the periodic table is shown here. A fuller version is shown on p. 99.

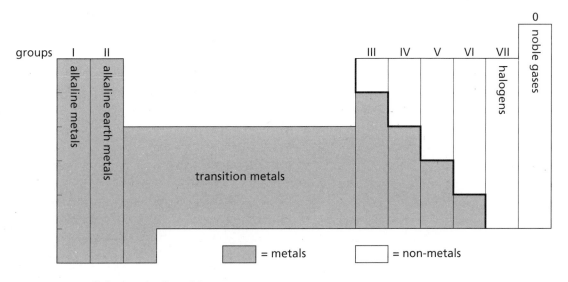

A summary of the periodic table

Properties of metals and non-metals

Metals	Non-metals
Are solids at room temperature (except mercury) and mostly have high melting points (excluding group 1 metals, mercury and cadmium)	Can be solids, liquids or gases – generally have low melting and boiling points (except carbon and silicon)
Are shiny when freshly cut	Are usually dull
Are strong and hard	Some are strong, others are weak
Can be bent or hammered into shape (malleable) or drawn into wires (ductile)	When solid, are usually brittle and crumbly
Are good conductors of heat and electricity	Are usually poor conductors of heat and electricity
Form alloys with other metals, giving them different properties	

Group I – the alkali metals

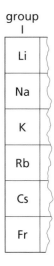

group I

Li

Na

K

Rb

Cs

Fr

- All have 1 electron in the outermost energy level which can be lost easily, forming a positive ion (see p. 22).
- All react with water, liberating hydrogen and forming soluble alkaline hydroxide solutions.
- The elements get more reactive as you go down the group. This is because the outer electron is further from the nucleus and therefore less strongly attracted to it, so it can be lost more easily in a chemical reaction.
- The melting and boiling points decrease as you go down the group, because the attractive force of the nucleus which holds the outer electron decreases as the number of layers of electrons increases. The outermost electron is less able to hold atoms together as a solid. This means that they can more easily be separated (see p. 27).

Group VII – the halogens

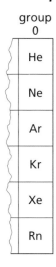

group
VII

| F |
| Cl |
| Br |
| I |
| At |

- All these elements are non-metals.
- All are diatomic molecules (made up of pairs of atoms, like Cl_2) (see p. 24).
- All have coloured vapours.
- All have 7 electrons in the outermost energy level.
- All react with metals, forming negative ions.
- All react with non-metals, forming covalent bonds (see p. 24).
- All react with hydrogen, producing gases which form acidic solutions when dissolved in water.
- They become less reactive as you go down the group. Fluorine is the most reactive since the outermost energy level is nearest to the nucleus, so it has the strongest attraction to any electrons in other atoms that are waiting to form bonds.
- A more reactive halogen can displace a less reactive halogen from a solution of its salt. For example, fluorine can replace the chloride ion in sodium chloride, producing sodium fluoride and chlorine.
- The melting and boiling points increase as you go down the group, because the molecules get larger so the intermolecular forces of attraction increase.

Group 0 – the noble gases

group
0

| He |
| Ne |
| Ar |
| Kr |
| Xe |
| Rn |

- These are unreactive (**inert**) gases, since their outermost energy levels are full and cannot take on or lose any electrons.
- They are therefore monatomic, existing as single atoms instead of molecules.
- Since they are unreactive, they are used when an inert atmosphere is required. For example, argon is used to fill light bulbs so the tungsten filament cannot react with anything.

Transition metals

This section of the periodic table includes the 'typical' metals in common use, such as iron and copper.

- They have high melting points.
- They are often used as catalysts.
- They form coloured compounds.
- They have several **oxidation states (valencies)** (see p. 22).

> *(Oxygen (group VI) reacts with most elements, forming oxides.*
>
> - *Oxides of metals are basic – they neutralise acids.*
> - *Oxides of non-metals are acidic – they neutralise bases.)*

Example questions

3.1   Will lithium or sodium react more violently with water? Explain your answer.

3.2   Why do you think that sodium and potassium are stored under oil?

3.3   What do you see when chlorine is reacted with sodium bromide?

3.4   Would you see any change when bromine is mixed with sodium chloride?

atomic structure and bonding

Inside an atom

An **atom** is the smallest divisible unit of any substance that can still be identified as that substance. Everything is made up of atoms. But, an atom is made up of smaller particles.

Protons, neutrons and electrons

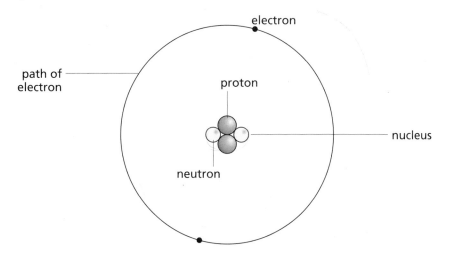

A simple model of an atom

The cluster of particles in the middle is called the **nucleus**. It is made up of **protons** (positively charged particles, 1+), and **neutrons** (particles with no charge). **Electrons** appear almost like clouds, moving around the nucleus at a very high speed. They are negatively charged (1–). These electrons are what are involved in a reaction.

Protons and neutrons are about the same mass, but the electrons have an extremely small mass – almost no mass at all!

> *(All these particles are shown in the diagram, but note that in reality the nucleus is very, very small compared with the overall size of the atom – like a football inside Wembley Stadium!)*

As we read through the periodic table in order (see p. 99), each element has one more proton than the last. So, we say the periodic table is in order of the number of protons, or the **atomic number**. If we take hydrogen, the first and simplest atom, it has one proton in the nucleus. This will give it a charge of 1+. However, atoms are only atoms when they are neutral, so it has one accompanying electron to make it neutral. A 1– charge neutralises a 1+ charge. The same follows for all the atoms, which have the same number of electrons as protons to make them neutral.

That is the easy part. Now for the slightly more difficult part …

Isotopes

The number of neutrons in the nucleus can vary slightly. Since they have no charge, they do not alter the charge of the atom, therefore, in theory, we can have as many as we want in an atom. Indeed, many elements do have atoms with different numbers of neutrons. These are called **isotopes**. They are atoms of the same element having the same number of protons, but different numbers of neutrons. Hydrogen, for example, has no neutrons in the nucleus. But an isotope of hydrogen, deuterium, has one neutron in the nucleus. Isotopes of an element have the same chemical properties, because they still have the same number of electrons in the outer shell, but different masses because there are either more or fewer neutrons.

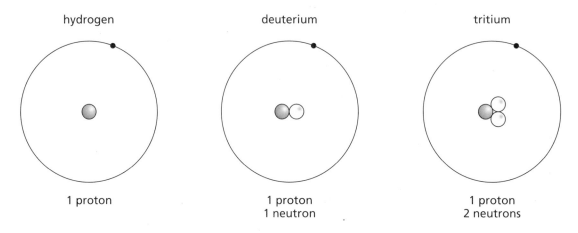

hydrogen	deuterium	tritium
1 proton	1 proton 1 neutron	1 proton 2 neutrons

The three isotopes of hydrogen

Relative atomic mass

The mass number of an atom can be worked out if you know the number of protons and neutrons in the nucleus. All you need to do is add the number of neutrons to the number of protons and the result is the mass number. However, chemists are more concerned with the **relative atomic mass** of an element. Since an element can have several isotopes, the mass number of the isotopes will vary slightly. A weighted average is taken, bearing in mind the proportions of each isotope. So, chlorine has two major isotopes. In a sample of chlorine gas, 75% of the atoms have a mass of 35 and the rest have a mass of 37. The relative atomic mass of chlorine is 35.5.

> *(Please note that when consulting a data book in an exam, the periodic table may give only the mass of the commonest isotope. Use the correct page in the data book to find the relative atomic masses.)*

Electronic structure

As we have already seen, atoms have the same number of electrons as protons. Electrons have a very specific arrangement around the nucleus and exist in **energy levels** or 'shells'. The first shell is closest to the nucleus and can hold 2 electrons, the second 8 and the third (for the purposes of GCSE) 8 electrons. The shells fill up, starting with the closest to the nucleus, until there are as many electrons as there are protons. Only the outermost energy level is involved in chemical reactions.

For example, the atomic number of chlorine is 17. It has 17 protons and therefore 17 electrons. The first shell is filled, leaving 15 electrons. The second shell is filled, leaving 7 electrons. These remaining 7 electrons are in the third shell. So, the electron arrangement of chlorine is 2,8,7. For GCSE, you need only know the electron structures of the first 20 elements, up to calcium, which is 2,8,8,2 (see p. 23).

When a reaction occurs, some electrons may be lost or gained from the original neutral atom, leaving it positive or negative. If a chlorine atom gains an electron, making it a negatively charged chloride **ion**, Cl^-, then its new electron arrangement is 2,8,8, the same as the noble gas argon. Hence, it has a full outer shell.

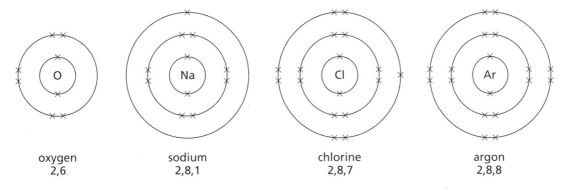

oxygen	sodium	chlorine	argon
2,6	2,8,1	2,8,7	2,8,8

Diagrams of the electronic structure of some common atoms

Bonding

The idiot's guide to bonding

Bonding is one of the most important ideas to understand in chemistry. Many people have difficulty understanding it, even though it is quite easy and logical. All you need to remember is one simple rule:

Happiness is a full outer shell!

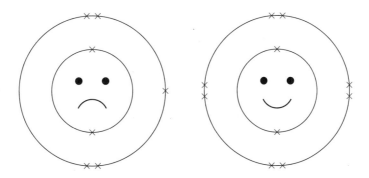

Just as we might strive for success, atoms strive for a full outermost shell. They can achieve this by bonding.

Bonding in substances occurs in two forms – **ionic** and **covalent**. It is easy to remember which form of bonding applies for particular compounds, as ionic bonding occurs between a metal and a non-metal and covalent bonding occurs between two non-metals.

Even without knowing anything about electrons, you can work out the formulae for a wide range of ionic compounds. All you need to know is their **valency** or charge. These can be found in the Appendix (see p. 100). For example, chloride is shown as Cl^-, so its charge is 1–. Aluminium is Al^{3+}, so it has a charge of 3+. When a substance is formed, the charges need to cancel out. For every positive charge, you need a negative charge.

So, for aluminium chloride, the aluminium ion needs three negative charges to cancel out its 3+ charge, so it grabs hold of three chloride ions, each with a single negative charge ($3 \times 1–$). Hence, the formula is $AlCl_3$.

> (**Valency** is the combining power of an ion – in other words, a measure of the bonds it makes with other ions. This is equal to its **charge**.)

Ionic bonding

Ionic bonding takes place between metals and non-metals. It involves the **giving or taking of electrons** from the outermost energy level in order to achieve a full outermost shell. Since we are not concerned with the other energy levels of electrons, we tend not to draw them on dot-and-cross digrams.

Example 1

If you react lithium with fluorine you get lithium fluoride, LiF. It is easier to see how LiF is made by looking at the electron arrangements.

> *Lithium has the arrangement 2,1.*
> *Fluorine has the arrangement 2,7.*

Now, decide how it is best for each atom to get a full outermost shell. The lithium could gain 7 electrons from the fluorine, getting the arrangement of 2,8, and the fluorine would have the arrangement 2. Alternatively, the lithium could lose its one outer electron to the fluorine. So ask yourself, 'is it easier to lose 7 electrons or gain 1?' The answer is quite obvious that it is easier to gain 1. In fact, it is always the metals that give away their electrons to the non-metals.

Since the lithium loses an electron, it becomes positively charged (Li^+). The fluorine gains one electron, so it becomes negatively charged (F^-). This is shown below as a dot-and-cross diagram.

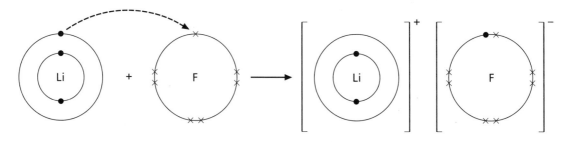

Ionic bonding in lithium fluoride

In the same way, magnesium would donate 2 electrons to oxygen for both to achieve a full outermost shell ($Mg + O \rightarrow Mg^{2+} + O^{2-}$).

Example 2

Calcium (2,8,8,2) has 2 electrons waiting to be given away and fluorine (2,7) needs to gain only 1 electron for a full outermost shell. Can you guess what will happen if you react calcium with fluorine? Well, start with the valencies (Ca is 2, F is 1) and work out the formula of calcium fluoride. It turns out to be CaF_2. So, there are 2 fluoride ions to each calcium ion. This means that the calcium atom gives away one electron to each fluorine atom, as shown in the dot-and-cross diagram below.

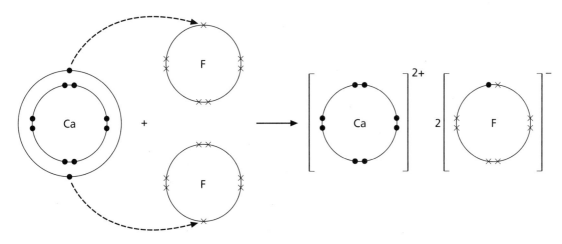

Ionic bonding in calcium fluoride

Properties of ionic compounds

From physics, we know that positive and negative charges attract. The same is true for ions. So, the Li^+ ion strongly attracts the F^- ion. In fact, every Li^+ ion attracts six F^- ions and vice versa, resulting in a regular arrangement which forms a **giant structure** known as an **ionic lattice** or crystal lattice. The strong attractive forces between the ions in these crystals mean they have high melting and boiling points. Also, because the ions in the solid are not free to move around they do not conduct electricity.

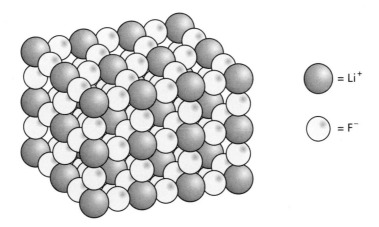

= Li^+

= F^-

Lithium fluoride ionic lattice

However, when an ionic lattice is dissolved in water, the water molecules surround the ions and weaken the forces holding the lattice together. The ions are free to move over each other so the solution can conduct electricity. Likewise, when the solid is melted the ions can move, so electricity can be conducted.

Covalent bonding

Covalent bonding takes place between non-metals. It involves the **sharing of pairs of electrons**. One electron from each atom is shared and the pair acts like glue, holding the two atoms together by attracting the nuclei. In some covalent molecules, atoms share several pairs of electrons, each pair representing one covalent bond.

Example 1

Hydrogen has one electron in its outermost energy level and needs another one to have a full outer shell and be happy. So, along comes another hydrogen atom and each shares its electron, so between them they both have a full outer shell.

Covalent bonding in a hydrogen molecule

Example 2

An oxygen atom has 6 electrons in its outer energy level, so it needs 2 electrons, which come from another oxygen atom. Each atom shares 2 of its electrons, producing a **double bond**.

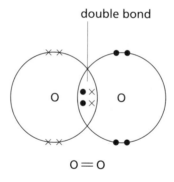

An oxygen molecule

Example 3

Nitrogen has 5 electrons in its outermost energy level. It therefore needs 3 more. So, along comes another nitrogen atom and each shares 3 of its electrons. These 3 electron pairs represent an extremely strong **triple bond**. In order to react, this triple covalent bond must be broken, which is very difficult. This explains why nitrogen is so unreactive.

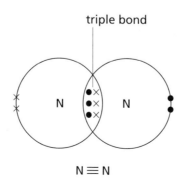

A nitrogen molecule

More examples

The syllabus expects you to know how to represent covalent bonds for water, ammonia, hydrogen, hydrogen chloride, methane and oxygen as dot-and-cross diagrams or as 'line diagrams', in which each line represents a covalent bond. Note that these diagrams only show the bonds, not the 3D structure.

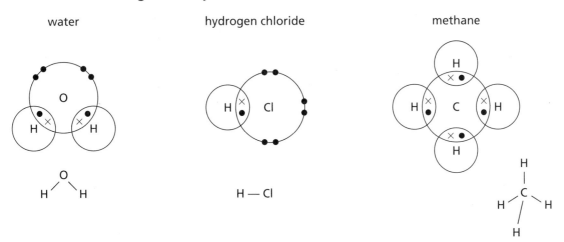

Some covalent molecules

Properties of covalent substances

Although the actual covalent bonds within each molecule are very strong, the **intermolecular forces** between the molecules (**van der Waals forces**) are very weak, so little energy is required to overcome these forces. Covalent substances therefore have low melting and boiling points. This is why many non-metals are gases or liquids.

> *(To summarise, bonds* within *a covalent molecule are strong, but forces* between *molecules are weak.)*

Most covalent molecules are not soluble in water because they do not break up into ions like ionic substances. However, some react with water to form ions, such as hydrogen chloride which forms hydrochloric acid in water.

When molten, covalent substances do not conduct electricity because they do not exist as separate charged ions which can carry charge.

Macromolecules

Some non-metals cannot form full outer shells by bonding with one, two or three other atoms. Carbon, for example, has 4 electrons in its outer shell and needs 4 more – quadruple covalent bonds are not possible! So it goes on bonding in all directions, in theory for ever! This results in a **giant structure** or **macromolecule** which is very, very strong. It takes huge amounts of energy to break the covalent bonds, so these solids have very high melting and boiling points. They are all insoluble and do not conduct electricity – except for graphite (shown overleaf).

The best examples of macromolecules are the **allotropes** of carbon (see page 26), sand (silicon dioxide) and various polymers (see p. 62).

Allotropes of carbon

Carbon can exist in different forms called **allotropes**. These all behave in the same way chemically, but their structures are very different, producing different physical properties. Graphite is a black, soft solid, whereas diamond is clear and extremely strong.

Diamond

Each carbon atom in diamond is covalently bonded to another 4 carbon atoms, forming a tetrahedral structure. The 3D structure is very rigid and diamond is therefore very strong, and has a very high melting point.

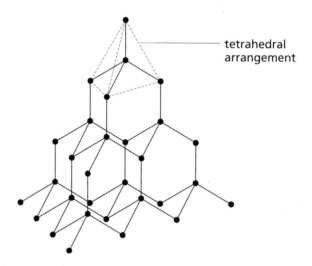

The macromolecular structure of diamond

Graphite

Graphite consists of layers of massive flat sheets of carbon atoms. Each carbon atom is covalently bonded to 3 other carbon atoms, forming honeycomb-shaped layers. Only 3 of the 4 electrons available for bonding are used covalently. The 'spare' electrons (**delocalised electrons**) are free to move between the layers, so graphite can conduct electricity.

The attraction between layers is much weaker than the covalent bonds within the layers, so layers of graphite can slide over each other easily. This is what happens when you use a pencil and is why graphite acts as a good dry lubricant.

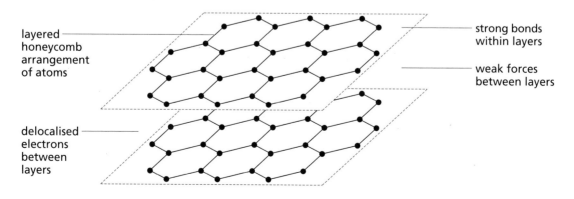

The structure of graphite

Metals

Metals can be regarded as giant structures of metal ions surrounded by free electrons. The outer electrons of each atom are delocalised and free to move, so they can conduct electricity. These **delocalised electrons** act as the 'glue' sticking the metal ions together. The structure of metals is often referred to as 'ions in a sea of electrons', which is quite accurate. It helps you appreciate that the ions are free to slide over each other, so metals can be stretched and bent.

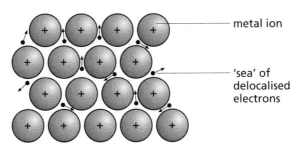

metal ion

'sea' of delocalised electrons

The giant structure of a metal

Example questions

4.1 If magnesium has an atomic number of 12 and an atomic mass of 24, how many neutrons has it got?

4.2 Write down the electron structure of the following:
(a) sulphur   (b) potassium   (c) magnesium ion   (d) oxide ion

4.3 Give the formula of the compound formed when deuterium reacts with oxygen.

4.4 Write down the formulae of the following:
(a) sodium nitrate
(b) calcium chloride
(c) sulphur dioxide
(d) sulphuric acid

4.5 Write down the names of the following:
(a) KNO_3
(b) Li_2SO_4
(c) NH_3
(d) HNO_3

4.6 Explain why sodium oxide melts at a higher temperature than sulphur dioxide, relating your answer to the type of bonding involved.

4.7 Explain the meaning of the following:
(a) isotope
(b) allotrope (careful!)
(c) macromolecule
(d) ion

> (**Hint**: you will need to look up valencies in the appendix to answer these questions.)

The reactivity series of metals

The **reactivity series** (see appendix, p. 102) is an order of reactivity of metals that has been produced by observing how violent their reactions are with air, cold water, hot water, steam and dilute acids – if such reactions occur at all.

Reaction with air

Potassium and sodium both react so readily with oxygen that they have to be stored under paraffin to stop them from coming into contact with the air. Metals above copper in the reactivity series react with air to form oxides:

$$4Na + O_2 \rightarrow 2Na_2O$$

Copper itself reacts extremely slowly with oxygen, but metals below it in the series are unreactive.

Reaction with water

When reacted with water, reactive metals such as potassium and sodium melt and float on the surface of cold water. They move around the surface of the water and fizz, producing hydrogen and the metal hydroxide. Less reactive metals such as calcium also react, but do not melt.

$$2K + 2H_2O \rightarrow 2KOH + H_2$$

$$Ca + 2H_2O \rightarrow Ca(OH)_2 + H_2$$

Note that calcium hydroxide is insoluble so a white **precipitate** forms.
Less reactive metals show little or no reaction with cold water, but some react with steam, producing the metal oxide and hydrogen.

$$Mg + H_2O \rightarrow MgO + H_2$$

Others react much more slowly, like iron rusting, or not at all. That is why copper is used in plumbing for water pipes.

> *(Although you may think that aluminium is not particularly reactive, it is. When aluminium is exposed to air, a layer of aluminium oxide builds up on its surface, which prevents oxygen from getting to the metal underneath. It may therefore appear unreactive, though if the oxide layer is removed, it will readily react with water.)*

Reaction with dilute acids

It is extremely dangerous reacting potassium and sodium with dilute acids. Other metals which are more reactive than hydrogen react with dilute acids, forming hydrogen gas and the metal salt:

$$Zn + 2HCl \rightarrow ZnCl_2 + H_2$$

*(It is a common misconception that since reacting sodium with a dilute acid is extremely dangerous, it must be more dangerous when reacting sodium with a concentrated acid. Indeed, concentrated acids do behave in some very strange ways! If you consider how sodium reacts with a dilute acid, it is easy to deduce why it is so dangerous. For example, if a lump of sodium was dropped in some dilute sulphuric acid the outer layer of sodium would react, forming sodium sulphate and hydrogen. The sodium sulphate on the surface will dissolve in the water, revealing the next layer of sodium to react. But in a concentrated acid the water content is much lower. So it takes much longer for the sodium sulphate to dissolve and the reaction slows. **Having said that, do not try this reaction**. It is difficult to predict how concentrated the acid must be! However, you do not need to know any of this for the exam.)*

Oxidation and reduction

Before talking more about the reactivity series of metals, it seems worthwhile to talk about **reduction** and **oxidation**. At its simplest level, as suggested by its name, oxidation is gain of oxygen and reduction is loss of oxygen.

So, when magnesium is burned in oxygen, it is oxidised:

$$2Mg + O_2 \xrightarrow{\text{oxidation}} 2MgO$$

If a more reactive metal comes along later and snatches the oxygen from the magnesium (more on this later), it is reduced.

But, if we consider what is happening with respect to electrons for a moment, the magnesium is giving electrons away to the oxygen when it forms magnesium oxide. So it is losing electrons. The oxygen is gaining electrons. Magnesium would also lose electrons if it reacted with chlorine, and the chlorine would gain one. So, in both cases, the metals are losing electrons, and the non-metals are gaining.

This means that for magnesium and oxygen reacting:

$$2Mg + O_2 \rightarrow 2MgO$$

Magnesium is losing electrons to the oxygen:

$$2Mg \rightarrow 2Mg^{2+} + 4e^-$$

$$O_2 + 4e^- \rightarrow 2O^{2-}$$

This is the same as a reaction between magnesium and chlorine:

$$Mg + Cl_2 \rightarrow MgCl_2$$

Magnesium is losing electrons to the chlorine:

$$Mg \rightarrow Mg^{2+} + 2e^-$$

$$Cl_2 + 2e^- \rightarrow 2Cl^-$$

So, apart from having chlorine instead of oxygen, the same things are happening in both cases with respect to electrons (chemists try to explain a lot in terms of electrons!). Therefore, both cases are examples of oxidation of magnesium.

The broadest definition of **oxidation is the loss of electrons** and of **reduction is gain of electrons**. A handy mnemonic to remember this is OIL RIG:

Oxidation   **I**s   **L**oss
Reduction   **I**s   **G**ain

Look again at the reaction between magnesium and chlorine:

$Mg \rightarrow Mg^{2+} + 2e^-$

$Cl_2 + 2e^- \rightarrow 2Cl^-$

Magnesium is losing electrons (oxidation) and chlorine is gaining electrons (reduction) all in the same reaction. This is known as a **redox reaction**.

Some definitions
- A **reducing agent** is one that causes other substances to be reduced – it donates electrons, thereby being oxidised itself.
- An **oxidising agent** takes electrons from other substances, thereby oxidising them, and being reduced itself.
- A **redox reaction** is one in which one substance is reduced and another is oxidised in the same reaction.

Displacement reactions

Displacement reactions are really just redox reactions in disguise. If you take a solution of a metal compound and add a more reactive metal, the more reactive metal will act as a reducing agent. Being more reactive, it will take the place of the less reactive metal in the solution, displacing it.

For example, potassium is much more reactive than silver. *The following reaction is extremely dangerous and should not be performed!* If potassium is added to some silver nitrate solution, the potassium will displace the silver and the products will be potassium nitrate and silver:

$AgNO_3 + K \rightarrow KNO_3 + Ag$

These reactions can be regarded as a tug o' war, with the metals getting stronger as their reactivity increases. If the negative ion is in the middle, the stronger, more reactive metal will always tear it out of the hands of the weaker metal.

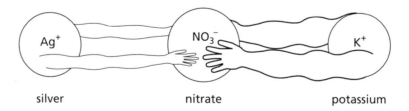

silver   nitrate   potassium

A displacement reaction

Example questions

5.1   I have some magnesium, aluminium, zinc and metal X. How would I go about finding out where metal X belongs in the reactivity series?

5.2   In the Thermit reaction, aluminium is reacted with iron(III) oxide, producing aluminium oxide, iron and lots of heat. Say whether or not it is a redox reaction and if so, what is being reduced and oxidised.

5.3   What will happen if hydrogen is passed over copper oxide?

topic six

rates of reaction

The good old kinetic theory is used to explain many things in chemistry, including why things boil. It is also used to explain how reactions happen.

Increasing the rate of reaction

When a chemical reaction occurs, the particles which combine need to meet up with each other (collide) so they can swap or share electrons. If you want to speed up a reaction, you need to get these particles to hit each other more frequently. So what can you do to help?

Increase the concentration of reactants in a solution
If you get some really dilute acid and an alkali in solution and imagine all the particles bouncing around at random you can appreciate that for a reaction to occur, the acid particles must hit the alkali particles before anything spectacular can happen. With the acid being very dilute, many of these collisions will be with harmless water molecules, which play no part in the reaction. So, you may have to wait a while for the appropriate particles to collide. However, if you increase the concentration of the acid, there are fewer water molecules to get in the way, so there are more useful collisions per second, so the reaction happens faster.

If gases are used in a reaction, their **concentration** can be increased by squashing them up (compressing them into a smaller space), so they do not have to go as far in order to meet the particle of a type that will react. Hence, increasing the pressure of gaseous reactants will increase the rate.

Break solid reactants up into small pieces
Reactions only occur on the surface of solid reactants. If a large lump is used, there is a lot of reactant to react, but not much surface for things to happen on. Breaking the lumps up into smaller pieces increases the available surface area for the reactants to meet on, so more reacting particles can collide per second and the reaction will be faster.

Increase the temperature
As discussed in topic one, increasing the temperature makes the particles move around faster. This means that the collisions will be harder (with more energy) and there will be more collisions per second. Reactions can only happen if the collision is hard enough (therefore having enough energy to react) for the reactants to combine. So, if more reactants collide hard enough, more collisions will result in a reaction. The minimum energy of a collision for a reaction to happen is called the **activation energy** (see p. 40).

Use a catalyst

Catalysts are substances which speed up a reaction without being used up. At the end of a reaction, there is the same amount as there was at the beginning of the reaction. Catalysts increase the rate of a reaction either by providing an alternative route for the reaction to take (with a lower activation energy) or by providing a surface on which the reactants can stop, meet and react.

> *(The rate of reaction is extremely important in the chemical industry because the faster a reaction happens, the more stuff is made, which can be sold. However, as you will see in the Haber process (see p. 70), it is often more costly to try to increase the rate of a reaction than the eventual gain from the increased rate.)*

Measuring the rate of reaction

It is important in GCSE chemistry to be able to interpret graphs of the rate of reaction. The rate of reaction can be measured by how long it takes for the reaction to finish, or by the rate of production of products (which is particularly easy if gases are produced). The steeper the graph, the faster the reaction.

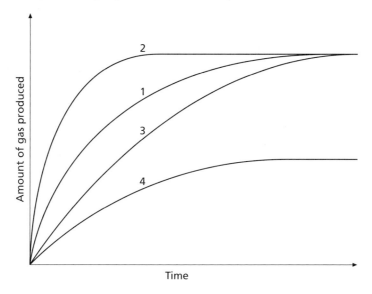

Rates of reaction between carbonate and acid

This graph shows how much gas is produced in a reaction between chips of an insoluble carbonate and an acid.

*   The same amount of gas is produced each time for graphs 1, 2 and 3, so the same amounts of reagents are also used.
*   Curve 1 shows the **base rate**.
*   Curve 2 starts steeper than curve 1, which shows that the rate started faster, so either smaller pieces of solid were used to increase the surface area or the acid was more concentrated.
*   Curve 3 shows a lower rate, so the solid may have been in a larger piece or the acid may have been more dilute.
*   Curve 4 shows only half the amount of gas produced, so half the amount of carbonate may have been used.

Example questions

6.1 Look at the graph below. A reaction occurred between a carbonate and an excess of acid and the rate of reaction was measured. The same reaction was repeated under different conditions.

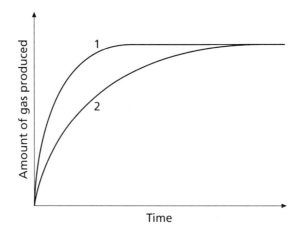

(a) Suggest how the conditions may have changed between the reactions and explain, using the kinetic theory of matter, why such changes in conditions would bring about the change in rate.

(b) Sketch on the same axes what would have happened if half the amount of carbonate was used.

acids, alkalis and salts

Chemists are always looking at how they can compare properties of different substances. Substances which dissolve in water can be classified as either **acid**, **alkali** or **neutral**.

Acidity and alkalinity

All metal oxides and hydroxides are **bases**. Those which dissolve in water are known as alkalis – they neutralise acids to produce a metal salt and water. Non-metal oxides that are soluble produce acidic solutions.

The **pH scale** measures how acidic or alkaline a solution is. It goes from 0 to 14. pH 0 is a very strong acid and pH 14 is a very strong alkali. pH 7 is neutral. To determine pH, **indicators** can be used, which change colour depending on the pH of the solution. The diagram shows the colour range for universal indicator.

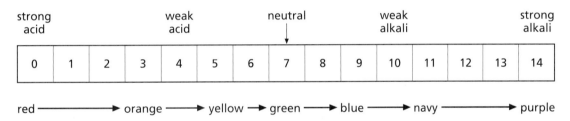

Universal indicator and the pH scale

Acids

- Acids turn universal indicator red or yellow, and turn blue litmus red.
- They react with reasonably reactive metals to form hydrogen and a salt. For example:

  $Mg + 2HCl \rightarrow MgCl_2 + H_2$

- They react with oxide and hydroxide alkalis and bases to form a salt and water only. For example:

  $CuO + H_2SO_4 \rightarrow CuSO_4 + H_2O$　(oxide base)

  $NaOH + HCl \rightarrow NaCl + H_2O$　　(hydroxide alkali)

- They react with carbonates and hydrogen carbonates to form carbon dioxide, a salt and water. For example:

  $ZnCO_3 + 2HCl \rightarrow ZnCl_2 + H_2O + CO_2$

  $NaHCO_3 + HCl \rightarrow NaCl + H_2O + CO_2$

- Acids are **proton donors**. They produce H^+ ions when dissolved in water.

Alkalis

- All metal oxides, hydroxides and carbonates are bases – they all neutralise acids. Soluble bases are known as alkalis. Alkalis produce hydroxide (OH^-) ions in solution with water.
- They turn universal indicator blue and purple, and turn red litmus blue.
- They neutralise acids, forming only a salt and water.

Strength and concentration

If you had a glass of orange squash with only a little water in it, you would call it strong. If you put in lots of water, you would call it weak. However, in terms of chemistry, the ideas of strong and weak mean different things.

When there is only a little water in the squash, chemists use the word **concentrated**. There are lots of orange squash particles and only a few water molecules. If there are lots of water molecules and only a few orange squash particles, chemists would call that **dilute**. This is the **concentration** of a solution. The higher the ratio of solute to solvent, the more concentrated it is. A concentrated acid has lots of acid particles in it and not many water molecules.

To chemists, **strong** and **weak** mean different things altogether. When hydrogen chloride gas is dissolved in water, as we have discussed, it forms H^+ ions and Cl^- ions almost completely. The H^+ ions are what makes it an acid. Not all acids completely split up into ions. For some acids, some of the molecules have split up into their constituent ions and others just remain as the molecules that they originally were, such as ethanoic acid (vinegar). When the molecule splits up, we say that it is **dissociated**. Almost all the molecules in hydrochloric acid are dissociated, so it is a strong acid, but relatively few molecules in ethanoic acid are dissociated, so it is a weak acid.

Salts

Salts are produced in neutralisation reactions of acids, alkalis, bases and carbonates. The salt produced depends on the acid used and the metal ion that was present in the alkali, base or carbonate.

For GCSE you need to learn the solubilities of certain salts, shown in the table.

Soluble salts	Insoluble salts
All sodium, potassium and ammonium salts	
All nitrates	
Most chlorides, bromides and iodides	Silver and lead chlorides, bromides and iodides
Most sulphates	Lead sulphate, barium sulphate and calcium sulphate (slightly)
Sodium, potassium and ammonium carbonates	Most other carbonates
Sodium and potassium hydroxides, and ammonia solution (ammonium hydroxide)	Calcium hydroxide (slightly), and most other hydroxides

Methods of preparing salts

For GCSE you should be able to describe the following methods of preparing salts, and of crystallising and extracting them, as described below.

Soluble salts

1. Reaction of a dilute acid with an excess of insoluble metal, insoluble base or insoluble carbonate. For example:

$$ZnCO_3(s) + 2HCl(aq) \rightarrow \textbf{ZnCl}_2(aq) + H_2O(l) + CO_2(g)$$

For this reaction, the carbonate is added to a beaker of acid until no more reacts. The resulting solution is filtered to get rid of the extra unreacted carbonate, then heated until it is a **saturated solution** (more on solutions later, see p. 48). As it cools, crystals of pure zinc chloride are deposited in the beaker. These can then be filtered off and dried with filter paper (*not* by heating).

2. Reaction of a dilute acid with exactly enough soluble base to just neutralise it. For example:

$$NaOH(aq) + HCl(aq) \rightarrow \textbf{NaCl}(aq) + H_2O(l)$$

Note that this is a **titration**. You must be able to describe how to do the following:

- Rinse a burette and fill it with acid.
- Record the volume of acid in the burette.
- Rinse a pipette with the alkali and then measure out exactly 25 cm³ of it into a conical flask on a white tile.
- Add a few drops of phenolphthalein indicator (which is pink in alkali and colourless in acid).
- Add acid carefully from the burette until the indicator just changes colour.
- Record the new volume of acid in the burette and use it to work out the volume of acid used.
- Repeat the titration to confirm results.

To obtain the salt repeat the titration, but this time not using any indicator. Follow the same steps as above to extract the crystals, saturating the solution, then filtering it and drying the crystals.

Insoluble salts

1. **Precipitation**. This is achieved by reacting two soluble salts to produce an insoluble salt. This method can also be used to remove unwanted ions from solution by precipitating them out and filtering them off, or to identify ions in solution by observing the colour of the precipitate (see p. 103 for details). For example:

$$AgNO_3(aq) + NaCl(aq) \rightarrow \textbf{AgCl}(s) + NaNO_3(aq)$$

Filter then wash and dry the precipitate to obtain the pure crystals.

2. **Direct synthesis**. Many salts have water molecules built into their structure. This is called **water of crystallisation**. Blue copper sulphate actually has 5 moles of water per mole of copper sulphate (moles are explained on p. 75). Heating it drives out the water, leaving white copper sulphate, but adding water makes it go blue again. So, if you want to prepare an anhydrous salt (i.e. without the water built

in) you need to perform the reaction without using any water. To do this, you usually start with the elements that make up the salt and react them directly. For example:

$2Al(s) + 3Cl_2(g) \rightarrow \mathbf{2AlCl_3(s)}$

Direct synthesis is really only performed for a few anhydrous chlorides which sublime, or for sulphides such as zinc or magnesium sulphide.

Example questions

7.1   What colour will universal indicator turn with the following solutions?
(a) sulphuric acid   (b) sodium chloride   (c) sodium hydroxide
(d) ethanoic acid   (e) ammonia

7.2   How do you best prepare the following salts?
(a) zinc chloride
(b) silver chloride
(c) potassium iodide (**hint:** *titration*)

   (OK, maybe the hint was just a bit of a giveaway!)

(d) iron(III) chloride (anhydrous)

7.3   Under which circumstances would direct synthesis of a salt be preferred over an acid/alkali reaction? If direct synthesis is not possible, how else might you be able to obtain an anhydrous salt?

energy transfer in chemical reactions

For almost every chemical reaction there is an energy change. This can be in the form of light or sound given out, but is usually a change in heat – either a rise or fall in temperature.

Exothermic and endothermic reactions

Exothermic reactions give out heat, so the surroundings get warm.
Endothermic reactions take in heat, so the surroundings get cold.

Exothermic reactions include:

- Combustion of fuels, for example:

  $$CH_4 + 2O_2 \rightarrow CO_2 + H_2O$$

- Respiration (a special case of oxidation):

  glucose + oxygen $\rightarrow$ carbon dioxide + water

- Neutralisation reactions
- Hydration of anhydrous (white) copper sulphate
- Reaction of concentrated sulphuric acid with water.

Endothermic reactions include:

- Dissolving some salts in water
- Photosynthesis (it follows, because it is just respiration in reverse):

  carbon dioxide + water $\rightarrow$ glucose + oxygen

- Decomposition of calcium carbonate:
  $$CaCO_3 \rightarrow CaO + CO_2$$

Bond energies

It is possible to predict how much energy is released or taken in for a reaction.
In order to break the original bonds of all the reactants, energy must be supplied.
When the new bonds form in the product, energy is released.

It is easy to understand that if more energy is given out forming new bonds than in breaking down the original bonds, then the reaction is *exothermic*; and if more energy is required to break the bonds than is given out forming the new ones, then the reaction is *endothermic*.

If you know the energy of individual bonds, then you can calculate the energy given off. To do this you need to understand **moles**. This is explained on p. 75.

For example, in the combustion of hydrogen:

$$2H_2 + O_2 \rightarrow 2H_2O$$

From experience, we all know that this reaction is exothermic. However, this can be calculated from the bond energies.

(Note that bond energies are given in kilojoules per mole of bonds broken/formed.)

So, 2 moles of hydrogen react with 1 mole of oxygen to produce 2 moles of water:

- Initially, 2 H—H bonds are broken. An H—H bond has an energy of 436 kJ = 2 × 436 = 872 kJ.
- Also, an O=O bond is broken = 498 kJ.
- So, the total amount of energy required in breaking the original bonds is 872 + 498 = 1370 kJ.

The new bonds formed are 2 sets of 2 O—H bonds = 4 × 464 = 1856 kJ.

- 1370 kJ of energy are put in to break the original bonds.
- 1856 kJ are given out when the new bonds form.
- So, the net energy change is 1856 − 1370 = 486 kJ per mole given out; the reaction is exothermic.

In an exam, you will be given the bond energies and asked to calculate the overall energy change and say whether it is endothermic or exothermic.

Energy level diagrams

This is a typical energy level diagram for an exothermic reaction.

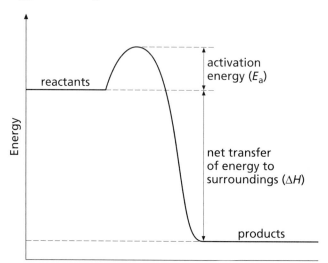

Energy levels in an exothermic reaction

Notice the curve of the line. It shows that to initiate the reaction, energy must be supplied. It will then continue by itself. The 'kick start' of energy needed to get the reaction going is called the activation energy (E_a). However, the overall change in energy of the reaction is given by the distance between the start and end lines. This net energy transfer is often shown as ΔH ('delta H').

Note that for exothermic reactions the product line is lower than the line showing the energy of the reactants. There is a net loss of stored bond energy – so energy is given out to the surroundings. Hence the products are lower in energy. For endothermic reactions the situation is reversed. Energy is taken in from the surroundings – there is a net gain of stored bond energy. Hence the products are higher in energy than the reactants. Can you think what the energy diagram for this might look like?

Catalysts work by lowering the activation energy for a particular reaction, so less energy needs to be supplied to 'kick start' a reaction.

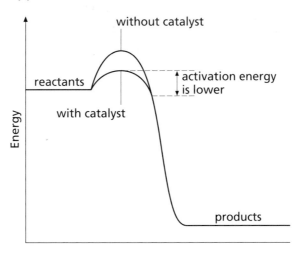

Using a catalyst

Example questions

8.1 When our muscles work harder, they respire much faster. Use this information to explain why we get hot when we exercise hard.

8.2 (a) Calculate the energy change when a mole of methane is completely burnt in oxygen. State whether the reaction is exothermic or endothermic.
   (b) Sketch an energy level diagram for the reaction.

Bond energies
(kJ per mole)
C—H = 435
O=O = 397
C=O = 803
O—H = 464

reversible reactions

Some chemical reactions can happen in both directions. In a simple reaction, two elements will combine to form a compound. In some cases, the product may break down, back into the original reactants. So, the reaction actually happens in both directions. Instead of using the usual $\rightarrow$ when writing a chemical equation, a $\rightleftharpoons$ is used to indicate that the reaction goes in both directions.

Equilibrium and yield

The rate at which the product is made and reforms into the original reactants balances out and an **equilibrium** is reached. This is when the product breaks down at the same rate as it is being formed, so a constant amount of product is present at any one time, though it is only a percentage of the amount that has the potential to be formed. The **yield** is the percentage of product formed compared with how much could form.

So, a **reversible reaction** can be seen as two reactions:

$A + B \rightarrow C + D$

$C + D \rightarrow A + B$

In general, this is represented as:

$A + B \rightleftharpoons C + D$

Examples of reversible reactions are the preparation of ammonia (the **Haber process**, see p. 70):

see p. 70

$N_2 + 3H_2 \rightleftharpoons 2NH_3$

Also, solutions of weak acids and alkalis can be regarded as equilibrium reactions. Since not all the molecules are dissociated and some molecules are reforming whilst others are ionising, the equation for a weak acid is:

$CH_3COOH + water \rightleftharpoons CH_3COO^- + H^+$

Several conditions affect the yield. The yield, and therefore the position of the equilibrium, shifts to minimise the effect of changing the conditions.

Shifting the equilibrium

(You may sometimes hear of the equilibrium shifting to the left or right. Since the original reactants are conventionally displayed on the left and the products on the right, if the equilibrium shifts to the right, then more product is formed, so the yield is higher.)

Changing temperature

Exothermic reactions. For reactions which give off heat, if the temperature is increased, the reaction will shift to resist the change. The yield will decrease because the reaction will go more in the endothermic direction, which is the direction that brings you back to the original reactants. Likewise, if the temperature is decreased, the yield will be higher.

It is sometimes beneficial to increase the temperature of an exothermic reaction even if the yield is slightly lower, because the reaction will be faster, so there may be more product in a given time. A compromise must be reached between the rate and the yield. In general:

$$A + B \rightleftharpoons C + D + heat$$

If the amount of A or B is increased, more C, D and heat are produced. Likewise, if the amount of C, D or heat is increased, the reaction goes more in the opposite direction and more A and B are produced.

Endothermic reactions. For reactions that 'take in' heat, increasing the temperature makes the reaction go more in the endothermic direction to 'cool off', which happens to be in the direction that yields more. Decreasing the temperature would decrease the yield. In general:

$$P + Q + heat \rightleftharpoons R + S$$

For the above reaction, if P, Q or heat is increased, more R and S are produced. Conversely, if R or S is increased, more P, Q and heat are produced.

Changing pressure

Not only can the effect of temperature be predicted, but also the effect of pressure on the equilibrium. For example, if a reaction starts off with one litre of gas and ends up with half a litre, there is a contraction. If the pressure is high before the reaction, squashing the gases up, then it will tend to react more in order to relieve the pressure, so the yield will be higher. On the other hand, if there is an expansion in a reaction and the pressure is high at the beginning, it will make it harder for the gases to expand at the end of the reaction, so the yield will be lower.

Example questions

9.1   Although, for the Haber process, it should be best to use as high a pressure as possible, suggest why the pressure used is only 200 atmospheres.

9.2   The reaction between nitrogen and hydrogen to form ammonia is highly exothermic. Therefore the lower the temperature, the higher the yield. Suggest why a temperature of 450°C is used, when it would make more sense to cool it as much as possible.

aqueous chemistry

Water, water everywhere

Water, we are told, covers more than two-thirds of our lonely little planet. All life depends on water. It seems such a simple molecule, with just two hydrogen atoms and one oxygen atom, yet its properties still continue to astonish chemists. If its boiling point was even a few degrees lower, life would not have been possible. It freezes at 0°C and boils at 100°C if it is pure. It can be purified by distillation. Tests for the presence of water are that it turns anhydrous (white) copper sulphate blue and blue cobalt chloride pink.

Anyway, water is an essential part of the atmosphere, and moves around the environment in a cycle. All air has a small percentage of water vapour in it (the humidity). Water in rivers and the sea evaporates in the heat of the Sun and rises through the air. When it gets quite high the air is much cooler, so the water vapour condenses into little droplets and forms clouds. As the clouds cool, the water droplets fall as rain, which falls back into rivers and into the sea and evaporates all over again. This is the **water cycle**. Oh, and while we are on the subject of rain, another thing which has baffled the greatest minds in history is why a torrential downpour only starts when you get out of the car and stops as soon as you get inside!

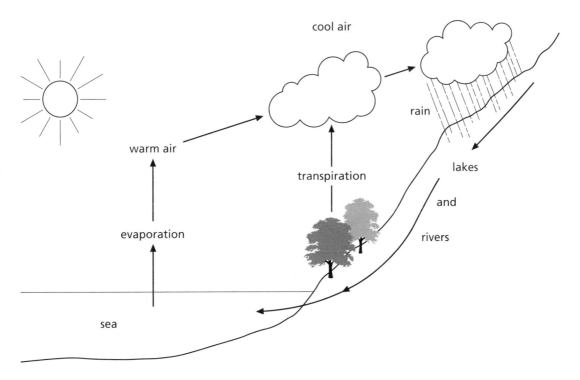

The water cycle

Not only is water extremely abundant, but it is also an important raw material for many industrial processes, as well as for domestic use:

- It is the most common solvent in the body, in the home and in the laboratory.
- It is easy to obtain, which means it is used in massive quantities as a coolant in power stations.
- It contains hydrogen, which can be extracted by reacting methane and steam. Hydrogen is very important in many industrial processes, such as the Haber process.

Hard and soft water

Natural water, including that which comes out of your tap, is not just H_2O. It often contains many other ions in solution. We are only concerned with ions that make water hard. To complicate matters further, there are two types of hardness of water. These are **temporary hardness** and **permanent hardness**.

What exactly does it mean if water is hard? Well, the answer is all to do with **scum**. If water is hard, adding soap will not produce a foamy lather, but a grey precipitate forms (scum). Only after adding excess soap will a lather begin to form.

Now for the science bit! Water hardness is caused by dissolved calcium and magnesium ions. These ions come from water flowing over limestone rock. The water is slightly acidic because it contains a little dissolved carbon dioxide. This reacts with the calcium carbonate in limestone, producing a solution of calcium hydrogen carbonate. Alternatively, the water may dissolve calcium or magnesium sulphate, making it hard.

Soap contains stearate ions, which are usually responsible for the lather produced. But when water contains calcium or magnesium ions, these ions combine with the stearate ions in soap and the calcium or magnesium stearate precipitates out because it is insoluble. So obviously, hard water is not always very beneficial.

So, to summarise:

$CaCO_3(s) + H_2O(l) + CO_2(aq) \rightarrow Ca(HCO_3)_2(aq)$ (forming hard water)

> *(Calcium hydrogen carbonate thermally decomposes and the reaction goes in reverse, forming 'scale' or 'fur' in a kettle.)*

With soap (St⁻ represents stearate ions):

$Ca^{2+}(aq) + 2St^-(aq) \rightarrow CaSt_2(s)$

Some areas have water supplies that are hard. People in hard water areas often have to take measures to remove the hardness of the water (see below). Detergents do not contain stearate ions, so even if you are in a hard water area, it is unlikely that there are problems with scum if you are using detergent.

Temporary and permanent hardness

Temporary hardness is so called because it is quite easy to remove from water. It is caused by the presence of calcium or magnesium hydrogen carbonate in solution. These hydrogen carbonates cannot exist alone as solids, so when the water is boiled they decompose, forming calcium carbonate, water and carbon dioxide. This removes the hardness. In hard water areas, people's kettles often 'fur up' with calcium carbonate that is produced from the decomposition of the hydrogen carbonate, so the heating elements have to be cleaned quite frequently:

$$Ca(HCO_3)_2(aq) \rightarrow CaCO_3(s)^- + H_2O(l) + CO_2(aq)$$

Permanent hardness cannot be removed so easily. It is caused by the presence of calcium or magnesium sulphate. To remove this form of hardness (or, indeed, temporary hardness) other methods must be used. The easiest is probably adding excess soap until all the calcium ions precipitate out and a lather can form. Distillation is another way of obtaining pure water, but it is extremely expensive and slow. Sodium carbonate (washing soda crystals) may be used to get those nasty ions to precipitate out:

$$Na_2CO_3(aq) + CaSO_4(aq) \rightarrow CaCO_3(s) + Na_2SO_4(aq)$$

In hard water areas, pipes are fitted with ion-exchange resins, as shown in the diagram.

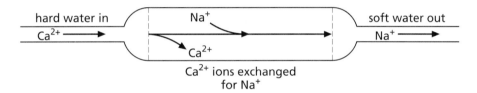

A simple ion-exchange system

This traps the calcium and magnesium ions and replaces them with sodium ions, which do not form scum when soap is added.

Aside from the disadvantages of hard water, there are some advantages. It contains calcium so if you drink it, it can help develop strong teeth and bones. It is also said to help reduce heart diseases and some say that it makes better beer, though that, I think, you should judge for yourself.

Water pollution

Fish and other water life rely on the small amounts of dissolved oxygen in water to live. Polluting water with fertilisers and untreated sewage causes plants to grow rapidly and die through competition for oxygen; the number of microbes increase to break down these dead plants, but in turn use up the dissolved oxygen so there is none available for fish.

Water can be polluted in other ways. The dumping of toxic waste kills water life. For example, aluminium ions block up fish gills. Acid rain can increase the pH of lakes and rivers, killing plants and animals. Even hot water from power stations is a danger as less oxygen can dissolve in hot water, so there is less available for water life.

Preparation of drinking water

Water that runs from the tap is not completely pure. But it is safe for human consumption. After water has been filtered to get rid of solid debris, extremely small quantities of chlorine are added to kill bacteria. In some areas, fluoride ions are added, which help you to develop strong teeth.

Solubility

Solubility is measured in grams of solute that dissolve per hundred grams of water (or whatever solvent is used). Solubility applies to gases as well as solids (ammonia gas is actually very soluble in water).

The solubility of solids depends on the temperature of the solvent. The higher the temperature, the more soluble it is. This can be explained by imagining what takes place when something dissolves. The water molecules knock the solute ions off and they 'float' around in the water. The higher the temperature, the faster the water molecules are moving (good old kinetic theory again!) so they are able to knock more ions off and take them into solution.

For gases, the cooler the solvent, the more soluble the gases are. Also, the higher the pressure, the higher the solubility. This can be explained by considering that gas molecules like to move around very fast. Cooling or compressing them slows them down or restricts their movement so they do not have enough energy to break free of a solution.

If a hot **saturated solution** is cooled, crystals of the solid gradually form. This is due to the fact that a solvent can hold more solute at a higher temperature. If it holds the maximum allowable solute at a high temperature and it is cooled, some of the solute must come out of solution because it simply cannot all stay dissolved at a lower temperature. This information can be used to plot solubility curves, as shown on the graph.

(When we say we are saturated, we usually mean that we are absolutely soaking wet. But chemists use this word differently. They use the term **saturated solution** *to mean a solution in which so much solute has been added, that if more were added, it would not dissolve at that temperature. And just to totally confuse matters, the word saturated is used in another way in chemistry, when talking about hydrocarbons (see p. 58). In general, saturated means 'full to capacity'.)*

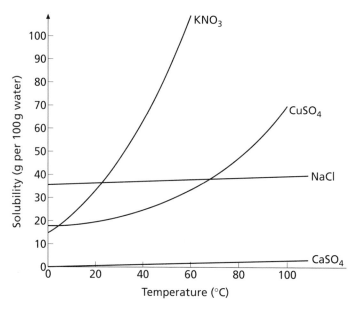

Typical solubility curves

Using these curves, it is possible to predict how much solute is deposited when a solution is cooled by reading off the solubilities at the higher and lower temperatures and subtracting them.

> *(Examiners are always looking to catch you out, so read the questions very carefully. Although most sane people quote solubilities in grams of solute per 100 g of water, a sneaky examiner will probably quote it per 25 g or 50 g of water, so watch out!)*

Example questions

10.1 What do you see happen if you boil calcium hydrogen carbonate solution?

10.2 Why is chlorine added to drinking water? Why is the concentration greater in swimming pools?

10.3 Suggest how ion-exchange resins which use sodium ions can be 'refilled' with sodium ions after the resin loses its effect.

10.4 Look at the solubility curve of compound X below. Calculate how much solid is deposited when a saturated solution in 25 cm³ of water is cooled from 80°C to 30°C.

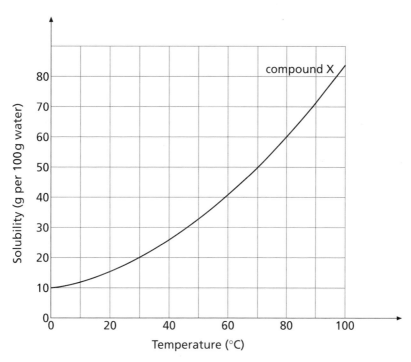

electrochemistry

An electric current is defined as the flow of charge. Physicists, being the sort of people that they are, narrow it down to the flow of electrons (negative charges), but chemists have a broader minded view and see it as the flow of charge, whether positive or negative. We already know that when we melt or dissolve ionic compounds, the ions are free to move around. So, it is conceivable that the charged ions can be encouraged to flow and hence carry an electric current.

Another thing that the physicists among you will note is that opposite charges attract – negative and positive are drawn together. Well this is at least one thing that chemists and physicists agree on!

Electrolysis

Take molten lead bromide as an example. Its ions are free to move. It is an **electrolyte**, able to carry charge. Now, if you get two **conductors (electrodes)**, made of graphite for argument's sake, stick both in the molten lead bromide and connect the other ends to a battery, a current will flow between the electrodes, since the charged ions between them are free to move.

This is called an **electrolysis cell**. The positive electrode is called the **anode**. The negative electrode is the **cathode**. Since opposite charges attract, and positive ions (**cations**) will move to the negative electrode (cathode) and negative ions (**anions**) will move to the anode.

(Remember – negative ions go to the anode.)

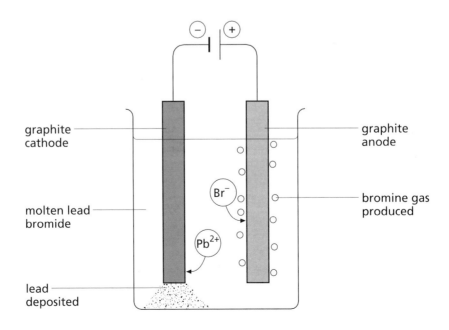

Electrolysis of molten sodium chloride

056378.

topic eleven – electrochemistry

Electrolysis of molten ionic compounds

Let's now consider what goes on at the electrodes during the electrolysis of molten lead bromide. At the cathode, there is a concentration of positive ions. Also on the cathode, there are electrons waiting to get out. The lead ion has a 2+ charge and the electrons each have a 1– charge, so it is beneficial for the lead ion to take on two electrons and become a lead atom. This is indeed what happens and the metal ion (which is always attracted to the cathode) often forms a coating on the cathode.

Likewise, at the anode, there are negative ions waiting to give electrons away. Since there is a deficiency of electrons at the anode, the negative bromide ions give away electrons and become atoms. In this case the bromide atoms form bromide molecules which are given off as a gas.

It is possible to write equations for what goes on at the electrodes. These equations are called ionic **half equations**.

- For lead bromide, at the cathode, the following reaction occurs:

  $Pb^{2+} + 2e^- \rightarrow Pb$ (the e^- refers to an electron)

- At the anode:

  $2Br^- \rightarrow Br_2 + 2e^-$

  Note that the above equation can also be written:

  $2Br^- - 2e^- \rightarrow Br_2$

Redox reactions

If we consider what oxidation and reduction are, we can relate them to electrolysis. Since positive ions at the cathode gain electrons, reduction occurs. Negative ions are oxidised at the anode, since they lose electrons (remember OIL RIG? see p. 30).

Electrolysis of ionic solutions

Things get a little more complicated in solutions. If an ionic compound is dissolved in water, you may not be sure what is formed at the cathode. Let's look first at the electrolysis of acidified water. The following exchanges of electrons take place:

- At the anode (positive electrode) oxygen gas is produced:

  $4OH^-(aq) \rightarrow 4OH(aq) + 4e^-$

  $4OH(aq) \rightarrow O_2(g) + 2H_2O$

  Overall, $4OH^-(aq) \rightarrow O_2 + 2H_2O + 4e^-$

- At the cathode (negative electrode) hydrogen gas is produced:

  $4H^+(aq) + 4e^- \rightarrow 2H_2(g)$

- Therefore:

  $4OH^-(aq) + 4H^+(aq) \rightarrow O_2(g) + 2H_2O(l) + 2H_2(g)$

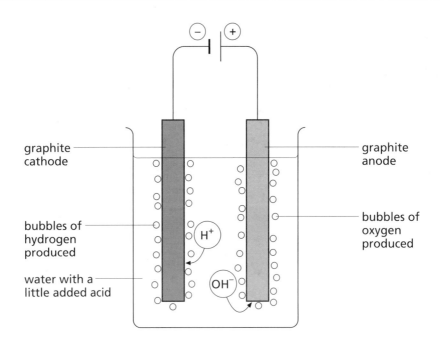

Electrolysis of acidified water

Now let's look at sodium chloride solution. There are two positive ions, the H^+ from the water and the Na^+ from the sodium chloride. There are also two negative ions, the OH^- from the water and the Cl^- from the sodium chloride. So which ions are deposited at the electrodes? The answer is the less reactive or less stable ion is deposited at the electrode. Sodium is very reactive. It likes to be combined with other things, and will therefore try to stay that way. Hydrogen is still quite reactive, but not as reactive as sodium, so it will form at the negative electrode instead of the sodium.

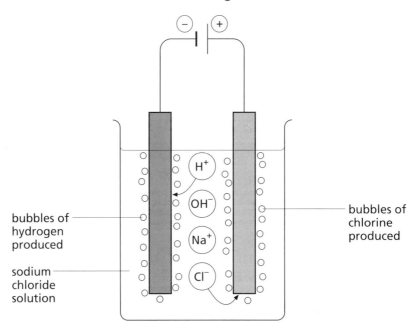

Electrolysis of sodium chloride solution

> (*To summarise, metals which are less reactive than hydrogen are discharged at the cathode. Metals which are more reactive than hydrogen are not discharged (hydrogen gas is discharged instead).*)

OH⁻ ions are more reactive than Cl⁻ ions, so the less reactive chloride ions lose electrons and are discharged at the positive electrode, rather than the OH⁻ ions.

For more information about this, see topic 13.

Uses of electrolysis

- Sometimes the conductor used as the cathode will be coated by the metal produced at it. This can be used for **electroplating** objects, such as with silver. The anode is made of the pure metal and the electrolyte used is a solution of a silver compound.

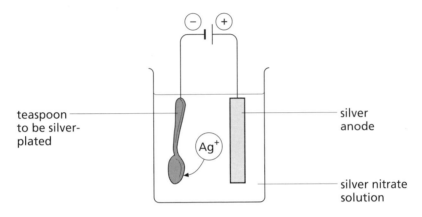

- Electrolysis can be used to **purify** metals such as copper. The anode is made of impure copper and the cathode of pure copper, in a solution of copper sulphate. Copper is transferred from the anode to the cathode.

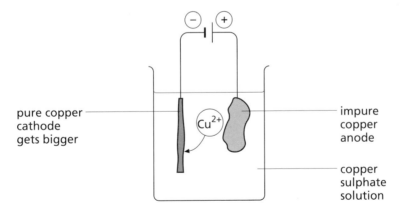

- Metals such as aluminium that are more reactive than hydrogen cannot be made by electrolysis in solution, because hydrogen gas would be made instead. However, they can be **extracted** from their molten ores using electrolysis (and very high temperatures!) (see p. 66).

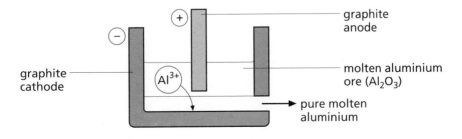

- Aluminium can also be **anodised** by electrolysis. As mentioned before, aluminium naturally has a layer of oxide coating it. This layer can be built up further by using aluminium for both electrodes in the electrolysis of dilute sulphuric acid. Oxygen produced at the anode reacts with aluminium just below the oxide coating, building up this layer even more.

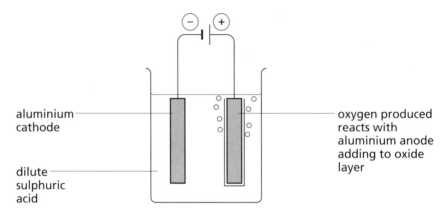

aluminium cathode

dilute sulphuric acid

oxygen produced reacts with aluminium anode adding to oxide layer

Example questions

11.1 Write ionic half equations for the reactions at the cathodes in the following reactions:

(a) electrolysis of copper chloride solution
(b) electrolysis of dilute hydrochloric acid
(c) electrolysis of aluminium oxide dissolved in cryolite

(**Hint:** see page 66)

11.2 Use your knowledge of the reactivity series of metals to explain why steel is sometimes electroplated with zinc (galvanised) to prevent it from rusting.

(**Hint:** steel is an alloy of iron and small amounts of carbon)

11.3 What would result if you attempted the electrolysis of liquid sulphur dioxide?

organic chemistry

Organic chemistry is all about carbon. In fact, it is all about the carbon found in living organisms, or substances formed from living organisms.

Fossil fuels

Energy sources are either **renewable** or **non-renewable**. Renewable energy (such as solar, wind and hydroelectric power) can be replaced in a relatively short space of time. Non-renewable energy sources (**fossil fuels**), on the other hand, take so long to be replaced that they can effectively run out.

There are three fossil fuels – coal, oil and natural gas. All are formed in the same way. Dead animals and plants are gradually covered over to become sedimentary rocks. Immense pressure and heat applied to these rocks over millions of years results in these organic remains being turned into coal, oil or natural gas. When burned, these fossil fuels release heat energy. However, once burned they are used up and it takes millions of years for them to be replaced.

> *(Wood is an interesting case. When burned as a fuel it is used up, but because new trees can grow in a relatively short space of time wood is a renewable organic energy source.)*

Burning organic compounds

- If any hydrocarbon is burned with a good supply of oxygen, no matter which organic substance it is, the only products are carbon dioxide and water. So, taking methane as an example:

  $CH_4 + 2O_2 \rightarrow CO_2 + 2H_2O$

  This reaction occurs in a roaring bunsen flame or in well maintained gas boilers.

- However, if there is not enough oxygen, then water and **carbon monoxide** are produced:

  $2CH_4 + 3O_2 \rightarrow 2CO + 4H_2O$

  This occurs in badly adjusted gas boilers. Carbon monoxide gas is very dangerous – people can become very ill or even die if their boilers are badly maintained and spewing out carbon monoxide fumes.

- If only a little oxygen is present, then carbon and water are produced:

  $CH_4 + O_2 \rightarrow C + 2H_2O$

  This occurs in the yellow bunsen flame when the air hole is closed. If you heat a test tube using a yellow flame, you will notice black carbon forming on the outside from the **incomplete combustion** of methane.

Pollution from fossil fuels

Carbon monoxide is poisonous. It takes the place of the oxygen in your blood, so less oxygen can get around your body. But don't worry! You don't get carbon monoxide from a bunsen flame. When it moves into an area where there is enough oxygen, it grabs another oxygen atom and becomes carbon dioxide.

$$2CO + O_2 \rightarrow 2CO_2$$

It is therefore referred to as a **local pollutant**, since when it gets into open air it becomes carbon dioxide.

Coal, oil and natural gas are all found naturally under the Earth's surface, so it is not surprising that they contain some impurities. These are mainly sulphur and nitrogen impurities. So when fossil fuels are burned they release sulphur dioxide and nitrogen oxides, as well as carbon dioxide and water. When released into the atmosphere, these pollutant gases dissolve in rain water and form **acid rain**, which damages the environment.

On a coal fire in the home, you may not be allowed to use coal straight from the mine. Instead, the coal is heated (careful – not burned!) to drive out the sulphur and nitrogen impurities. The purer coal formed is called **coke**. It may seem that coke is therefore non-polluting, but it can be looked at in two ways. Although coke does not contain the impurities, it means that for a given mass of coke, more carbon dioxide is produced than with an equal mass of coal.

Carbon dioxide is far from harmless – it is a **greenhouse gas** and a **global pollutant**, since it builds up in the Earth's atmosphere, where it does not change or react with other atmospheric gases. Like the glass in a greenhouse, it forms a layer over the Earth which traps heat from the sun and results in global warming.

Oil

Natural oil (called **crude oil** or petroleum) is found underground. As you know, oil floats on water because it is less dense. So, over time, it will rise up above the underground water found in porous rock (rock with little holes in that liquids and gases can seep through). Oil and natural gas eventually float above the water and continue to rise in the porous rock. They stop when there is non-porous rock above, through which they cannot flow. To collect the oil, all we need to do is drill through the non-porous rock, which releases the pressure of the oil so it flows up the pipe.

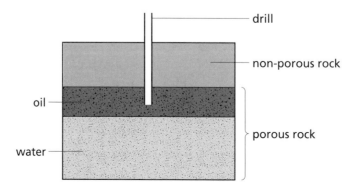

Drilling for oil

Crude oil, as its name suggests, is a mixture of all sorts of hydrocarbons. Some have very small molecules and others have massive molecules.

> *(Hydrocarbons are substances which contain hydrogen and carbon* only *(don't forget the* only *in an exam!).)*

The different sized molecules have different boiling points. So, they can be separated by **fractional distillation** (see p. 13). More **volatile** fractions (i.e. with lower boiling points) can be piped off from higher up the fractional column. Less volatile fractions (i.e. with higher boiling points) are extracted lower down. These fractions do not contain only one type of molecule, but a range of molecules with similar boiling points. It is very difficult to separate the oil into all its different types of molecules because the boiling points of the ranges are extremely close.

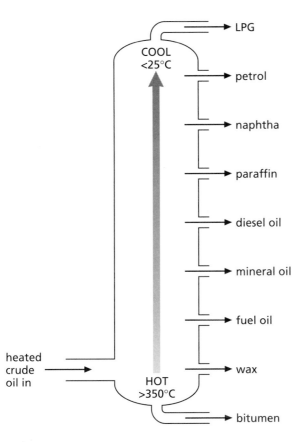

Fraction	Uses
Gases (liquefied petroleum gas)	Camping gas
Petrol (gasoline)	Car fuel
Naphtha	Petrochemical industry, cracking
Kerosene (paraffin)	Aircraft fuel
Diesel oil (gas oil)	Lorry and central heating fuel
Mineral oil	Lubricating oil
Fuel oil	Ship and power station fuel
Wax, grease	Candles and grease for bearings
Bitumen	Tar for roads or roofing

Fractional distillation of crude oil   *The main fractions of crude oil and their uses*

The fractions in the table are listed in ascending order of size. The properties of the molecules change gradually as the number of carbon atoms in them increases. As the molecules get larger:

- their boiling point increases
- they become less volatile
- they become thicker and more syrupy, so they flow less easily (are more viscous)
- they become less flammable and become harder to set on fire.

Larger hydrocarbons are extremely difficult to ignite. It is inefficient to use them as fuels as it takes a lot of energy to get them to burn. They also burn less cleanly than smaller molecules and deposit carbon as a result of incomplete combustion.

Cracking

It is possible to break molecules with long carbon chains into smaller ones. This process is called **cracking**.

Long-chain hydrocarbons are heated to a vapour state over a finely powdered **catalyst**, which supplies a very large surface area for the molecules to break down on. The large molecules break down into smaller molecules, though it is difficult to control precisely which smaller molecules are produced. As a result, the mixture of products is separated further by fractional distillation.

Carbon compounds

Alkanes

Alkanes are the group of hydrocarbons which are found in crude oil. A group of molecules with similar general formulae and chemical properties is called an **homologous series**. There is a gradual change in the physical properties of the members of homologous series.

When writing the formula for an alkane, the molecular formula is given. That is, although the ratios of carbon and hydrogen molecules can be cancelled down, they are not. For example, ethane is C_2H_6. This is not cancelled down to CH_3 because that is actually a different molecule (and an impossible molecule!). All alkanes have the general formula C_nH_{2n+2}.

All alkanes contain single covalent bonds only and are therefore described as **saturated** (nothing to do with solutions!).

Examples of alkanes are methane, ethane, propane and butane.

methane	ethane	propane	butane
CH_4	C_2H_6	C_3H_8	C_4H_{10}

Some common alkanes

(The naming of the hydrocarbons gives an indication of the structure of the molecule. Meth-, eth-, prop- and but- relate to 1, 2, 3 and 4 carbon atoms, respectively. After but- it is easy to work out what the name means as they come from the names of polygons: pent- from pentagon, meaning 5; hex- from hexagon, meaning 6, etc. The end of the word, in this case -ane means it is an alkane. If it ends in -ene, it is an alkene (see p. 60).)

Isomerism
Consider the first three alkanes for a moment. All the carbon atoms are joined in a line. Even if we were to draw propane in an L-shape, the carbon atoms would still be in a line. Remember that we cannot easily represent the 3D structures of molecules

on flat paper. Organic molecules are not really in straight lines or L-shapes, but it is the easiest and most convenient way to draw them. Now, consider butane. It is possible to draw a C_4H_{10} molecule, with its 4 carbon atoms and 10 hydrogen atoms in a different arrangement, as shown in the diagram. Note that each carbon atom must have four single bonds, and each hydrogen only one.

butane   2–methylpropane

Isomers of C_4H_{10}

The diagram of 2-methylpropane has the same **molecular formula** as butane, but a different **structural formula**. Unlike the butane molecule, which has the 4 carbons joined one after the other (linear), this has a branched shape. It is called 2-methylpropane for a very logical reason. The **propane** comes from the main part of the molecule, made up of 3 carbon atoms. The **methyl** part comes from the fact that the branched section consists of a single carbon group. The **2** at the beginning comes from the fact that the branched carbon atom is on the second carbon atom along.

The possibility of hydrocarbons having different structures, which may be branched, is called **isomerism** (no, not a New Age religion!). Isomers have the same molecular formula as each other but their structures are different (they will be branched differently).

Isomers of the same alkane all behave in a similar way chemically, because it is only the type of bond present that determines how they will react. But their physical properties are slightly different. It is easy to predict how the physical properties change. Just remember that the more branched the molecule, the lower the boiling point. This is all down to the surface area of the molecules. An unbranched isomer of an alkane has lots of surface area (think of it as a sausage). This means there is a lot of surface for molecules to come into contact with each other, so the molecules are quite strongly attracted, so a lot of energy is required to separate them. This means the boiling point is quite high. Now imagine a very branched isomer. It is likely to be more spherical (think of a ball with the same volume of a sausage) so there is less surface for molecules to come into contact with each other, therefore less attraction between molecules, so the boiling point is lower.

Alkenes

Alkenes are another homologous series of hydrocarbons. They are produced during cracking. To understand why, look at the equation for cracking butane:

$$C_4H_{10} \rightarrow C_2H_6 + C_2H_4$$

There just aren't enough hydrogen atoms to go around, so one molecule must make do with fewer hydrogen atoms than it would if it were an alkane. Because this molecule now has fewer bonds with hydrogen, it needs to use the extra bonds somewhere, so one carbon–carbon bond becomes a **double bond**. The molecule is called an alkene and has the general formula C_nH_{2n}. The first two alkenes in the series are shown in the diagram (think – why can 'methene' not exist?).

ethene
C_2H_4

propene
C_3H_6

Common alkenes

Alkenes are described as **unsaturated** hydrocarbons because not all their bonds are single bonds. Since hydrocarbons are much happier to have single bonds, this makes alkenes much more reactive than alkanes. When they react, the double bonds are broken and used to bond to something else. This is called an **addition reaction**. Common addition reactions include those with bromine, hydrogen, water and with themselves.

Addition reactions with bromine

A simple test for any unsaturated hydrocarbon is that it decolorises bromine water (which is orangey brown).

C_2H_4	$+ Br_2 \rightarrow$	$C_2H_4Br_2$
ethene	bromine (orange)	1,2-dibromoethane (colourless)

ethene   bromine   1, 2-dibromoethane

Addition reaction with hydrogen

Alkenes react with hydrogen to form their respective alkanes (no surprises there!). This reaction is called hydrogenation. It needs a little help from a nickel catalyst.

ethene   hydrogen   ethane

Vegetable oils (liquids) are unsaturated molecules. When reacted with hydrogen in the presence of a nickel catalyst, these oils harden, producing the solid we all know and love (well, perhaps not!) – margarine.

Addition reactions with water

Ethenes can react with water (well, actually steam, but that's a technicality because ethene bubbles through cold water without reacting). A strong acid catalyst is used (phosphoric acid) at a reasonably high temperature and pressure, forming alcohols.

ethene   steam
(water)   ethanol

Alkene – alkene reactions

Alkenes can react with themselves to form **polymers** – large macromolecules. This way of producing polymers is called **addition polymerisation** (no guesses why). The unsaturated alkenes are called monomers (*mono* means one, *poly* means many).

Polymers

The most simple polymer is a polymer of ethene called poly(ethene), often referred to as polythene. It is produced when ethene molecules are heated at high pressure, in the presence of a catalyst.

ethene   poly(ethene)

The n represents any number of ethene molecules.

Polymers produced by addition polymerisation have strong covalent bonds within the chains of carbon atoms, but only weak forces between the chains so they can be melted and moulded. They are unreactive and are good electrical insulators. They can be thermally decomposed if heated strongly. PVC or poly(chloroethene) is another common polymer. The presence of the chlorine atom changes its properties. It is made as follows:

chloroethene   poly(chloroethene)

Plastics

Plastics are types of polymers made of large tangled masses of polymer chains. There are two types of plastic:

- Thermosoftening plastics have weak forces between the polymer chains, so they melt easily. They can be remoulded when heated and harden when they are cooled.
- Thermosetting plastics can be heated once. When they are first heated, strong covalent bonds called **cross-links** form between the polymer chains. If they are heated again, these cross-links prevent the plastic from melting, so they cannot be remoulded. These plastics are useful when they are going to be used around high temperatures (like light-bulb sockets). Light-bulb sockets use a plastic called Bakelite®. These plastics are not made by addition polymerisation.

topic twelve – organic chemistry

Alcohols

Alcohols are another homologous series, which have the **functional group** –OH. A functional group is the group of atoms which gives a molecule its special properties. Methanol, ethanol and propan-1-ol are all alcohols.

methanol   ethanol   propan–1–ol

Ethanol is a good organic solvent and is the alcohol in alcoholic drinks. There are two ways of making it. One involves the reaction of ethene and steam (see p. 61) and the other is by using fermentation of sugars by yeast cells:

$$C_6H_{12}O_6 \rightarrow 2C_2H_5OH + 2CO_2$$

The **enzymes** in yeast which carry out the above reaction are **biological catalysts**. They have an optimum temperature of about 35°C, at which their rate of production of ethanol is the highest. Unfortunately, yeast cells die if the ethanol concentration is above about 15%, so after the reaction is finished, the ethanol is extracted by distillation.

Yeast is also used to make bread rise as it produces carbon dioxide bubbles. If they are overheated, the enzyme molecules in yeast responsible for fermentation are destroyed.

The two methods of producing ethanol have different advantages, as the table illustrates:

Method	Rate of reaction	Quality of product	Raw material(s)	Type of process
Hydration	Fast	Pure	Ethene from oil (finite resource)	Continuous (cheap on manpower)
Fermentation	Slow	Impure	Sugars (renewable)	Batch (expensive on manpower)

Alcohols are also quite reactive.

Oxidation

If an alcoholic drink is exposed to the air for a long period of time, the ethanol oxidises and the drink goes sour due to the production of ethanoic acid (vinegar). These acids are called **carboxylic acids** and have the functional group –COOH. Carboxylic acids are weak (partially ionised) acids.

$$C_2H_5OH + O_2 \rightarrow CH_3COOH + H_2O$$

ethanol   oxygen   ethanoic acid   water

Reaction with sodium

Ethanol reacts with sodium to produce sodium ethoxide and hydrogen.

$$2C_2H_5OH + 2Na \rightarrow 2C_2H_5ONa + H_2$$

Reaction with carboxylic acids

Alcohols react reversibly with carboxylic acids (with a catalyst of concentrated sulphuric acid) to produce **esters**. For example, ethanol and ethanoic acid produce the ester ethyl ethanoate and water.

$$C_2H_5OH + CH_3COOH \rightleftharpoons CH_3COOC_2H_5 + H_2O$$

Esters often have fruity smells and are used as flavourings in foods.

Example questions

12.1 Draw the three isomers of C_5H_{12}.

12.2 Write balanced chemical equations for the complete and incomplete combustion of ethane.

12.3 Name three fractions of crude oil in ascending order of boiling point, and give a use for each one.

12.4 The molecules below are isomers of octane. Identify which is octane itself and say which of the two isomers has the highest boiling point. Explain your answer.

12.5 Write a structural equation for the formation of poly(ethene) from ethene and state the conditions required for the polymerisation to take place. Name the type of polymerisation.

12.6 Which method of production is most suitable to produce ethanol for medical use? Explain your answer.

12.7 Why does wine taste sour when it goes off?

Extraction of metals

Oxygen, as we know, is a very reactive element. Most metals, apart from the least reactive metals (gold, silver and platinum), do not occur naturally. They are found in compounds, usually combined with oxygen. The naturally occurring compounds are the metals' ores. If we want to get the metals out, we need to reduce them. Many metals can be reduced by using reducing agents. Carbon (coke) is often used. For GCSE you need to know and understand the extraction of several metals.

Aluminium

Aluminium is the most abundant metal in the Earth's crust. Most aluminium ores do not have a high enough aluminium content to make extraction economical. **Bauxite**, its main ore, is the one from which aluminium is extracted.

Bauxite is impure aluminium oxide (Al_2O_3). The first step is to purify it. Aluminium is more reactive than carbon so it cannot be reduced by carbon. Instead, aluminium oxide is electrolysed (see p. 53). There are, however, a few considerations to take into account for the electrolysis of aluminium oxide:

- For electrolysis, as you should know, the ions must be free to move. They are only free when molten or in solution. Aluminium oxide does not dissolve in water and its melting point is over 2000°C. The energy required to heat it would make the process inefficient. So, aluminium oxide is dissolved in cryolite (Na_3AlF_6), another ore of aluminium. Cryolite melts at a lower temperature, so the electrolysis can occur at a lower temperature (about 1000°C).
- Graphite electrodes are used. Molten aluminium is produced at the cathode and sinks to the bottom of the cell, from where it is piped off.

  $Al^{3+}(l) + 3e^- \rightarrow Al(l)$

- Oxygen is produced at the anode. This means that the graphite electrodes are oxidised to carbon dioxide, so they waste away and must be replaced regularly.

  $2O^{2-}(l) \rightarrow O_2(g) + 4e^-$

- Electrolysis for the extraction of aluminium consumes large amounts of electricity.

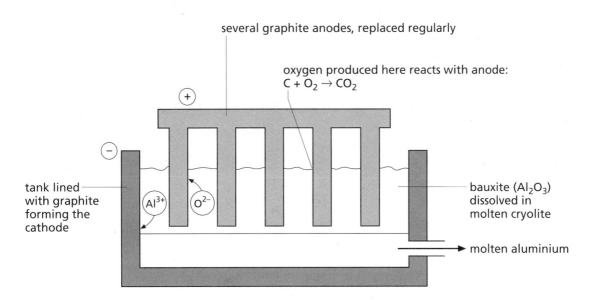

several graphite anodes, replaced regularly

oxygen produced here reacts with anode:
$C + O_2 \rightarrow CO_2$

tank lined with graphite forming the cathode

Al^{3+} O^{2-}

bauxite (Al_2O_3) dissolved in molten cryolite

molten aluminium

Extraction of aluminium by electrolysis

Aluminium is an extremely useful metal. It is a good conductor, is malleable, ductile and has a very low density. Although reactive, it resists corrosion because of the thin oxide layer on its surface, which prevents oxygen from getting to it. Because of its properties, aluminium has many uses.

Uses of aluminium

Use	Reasons
Kitchen foil	Resists corrosion, malleable
Window frames	Resists corrosion
Aeroplanes	Resists corrosion, low density
Car engines	Resists corrosion, low density
Power cables	Resists corrosion, low density, good conductor

Iron and steel

Iron is the second most abundant metal in the Earth's crust. Its ores are **haematite** (Fe_2O_3) and **magnetite** (Fe_3O_4).

It is extracted in a **blast furnace**, where a sequence of reactions takes place:

> *(Note that the sequence of reactions starts from the bottom upwards. All raw materials are added from the top and the products are collected at the bottom.)*

1. The raw materials (iron ore, coke and some limestone) are added to the blast furnace.

2. Hot air is blown into the furnace, oxidising the coke to produce carbon dioxide:

   $C + O_2 \rightarrow CO_2$

3. The carbon dioxide reacts with hot coke further up the furnace, producing carbon monoxide:

   $CO_2 + C \rightarrow 2CO$

4. The carbon monoxide reduces the iron ore, forming molten iron which flows to the floor of the furnace and is run off:

   $3CO + Fe_2O_3 \rightarrow 2Fe + 3CO_2$

5. Meanwhile the limestone decomposes to produce quicklime:

   $CaCO_3 \rightarrow CaO + CO_2$

6. The quicklime reacts with impurities in the ore such as sand, forming a molten **slag** which floats above the molten iron:

   $CaO + SiO_2 \rightarrow CaSiO_3$

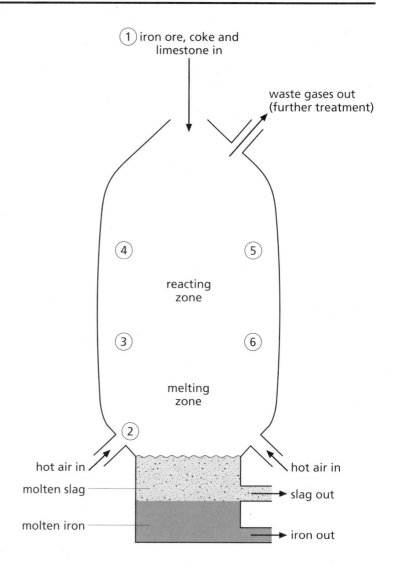

Extraction of iron in a blast furnace

The iron produced is tapped off at the bottom. It contains about 5% of carbon and is called cast iron or pig iron. If cooled in this state, it becomes very hard but also very brittle due to the high carbon content.

To remove impurities such as excess carbon, iron from the blast furnace is mixed with some limestone and burned with oxygen. All the oxides produced are acidic, being non-metal oxides, and most are gases which escape. The rest react with CaO (a basic oxide produced from the limestone). This is called the **basic oxygen process**. As a result, a molten slag forms on the surface of the molten steel and is run off.

The steel produced is an alloy of iron with some carbon. Its properties depend on the amount of carbon in the steel. The hardness of steel increases the more carbon it contains. However, the strength of steel 'peaks' at around 1% carbon.

Other metals may be added in small quantities to make different alloys with different properties. For example, chromium is added to make stainless steel. These added metals disrupt the metal lattice structure of the steel, altering its properties.

Type of steel	Properties	Uses
Mild steel (low carbon)	Soft and easily shaped	Car body panels, nuts and bolts
Medium carbon steel	Harder and strong	Hammers, axes, chains, pylons
High carbon steel	Hard but slightly brittle	Knives, scissors, razor blades, drill bits
Tungsten steel	Very hard and strong	Armour plating, tools for cutting metals
Stainless steel (i.e. with chromium)	Hard, does not corrode	Cutlery, car accessories, some tools

Rusting

Iron and steel react with oxygen, in the presence of water, forming rust. Rust is brittle, so it weakens the iron or steel. If salt is dissolved in the water, rusting occurs faster.

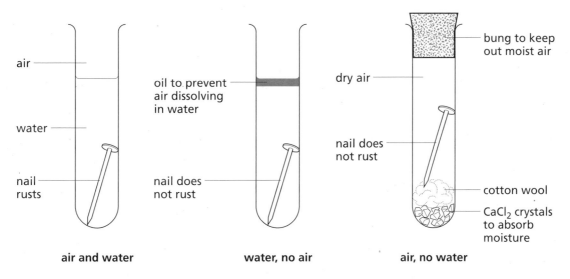

air and water　　　**water, no air**　　　**air, no water**

Demonstrating that iron rusts only in the presence of air and water

Rusting needs both air *and* water. So if steel is protected from either water or air, it does not rust. This is easily achieved by painting the metal. Greasing it will repel water and plating it in other metals will help. **Galvanising** is coating with zinc. Since zinc is more reactive than iron, oxygen or water will react with it in preference to the iron, thus protecting the steel.

Titanium

Titanium is a strong transition metal that is resistant to corrosion. Its low density and strength make it ideal for aircraft and space vehicles. It is also used in medicine for artificial hips as it is light and biologically inert.

Its ore is mainly composed of titanium dioxide. You might expect that it can be extracted in the same way as iron, but even small traces of carbon would make it brittle. Instead, a more reactive metal is used. First, it is converted to titanium chloride and then reacted with sodium or magnesium. This is carried out in an inert atmosphere (of argon) since it would react with air or moisture.

$TiCl_4 + 4Na \rightarrow Ti + 4NaCl$

Titanium is made in batches and this is therefore a **batch process**.

Copper

Copper is a relatively unreactive metal, so it is not difficult to extract from its ores. But when used as electrical cables it must be very pure, so it is purified by the electrolysis of copper sulphate solution (see p. 53). This results in copper which is about 99.95% pure. At the anode, a sludge containing silver and gold is deposited, which makes the process more economical.

Because copper is quite soft, it is a good conductor of heat and electricity and does not corrode. It is used extensively, especially in alloys as follows:

- in electrical wires
- in water supply and central heating pipes
- in brass, when alloyed with zinc
- in bronze, when alloyed with tin
- in coins, when alloyed with nickel
- to harden gold (18 carat gold contains 25% copper).

Production of compounds

Ammonia

Ammonia is produced in the **Haber process**. Nitrogen is a triple-bonded diatomic molecule and is therefore very stable and unreactive, so the Haber process is the only way to produce ammonia. It is a compromise, because the yield is low but ammonia is very important in making fertilisers, which contain nitrates or ammonium compounds (see p. 71).

In a nutshell, the nitrogen is taken from the air and the hydrogen is obtained from the reaction of methane and steam:

$CH_4 + H_2O \rightarrow 3H_2 + CO$

$(2CO + O_2 \rightarrow 2CO_2)$ (this reaction happens spontaneously)

Nitrogen reacts with hydrogen reversibly, to produce ammonia. It is an exothermic reaction.

$N_2 + 3H_2 \rightleftharpoons 2NH_3$

Since the reaction is exothermic, the yield would be higher if the temperature is low. But if the temperature is too low, the reaction would be very slow. A compromise of 450°C is used.

Now, if you look at the proportion of nitrogen to hydrogen in ammonia, you see it is 1:3. So the gases present in the reacting chamber are in the proportions of 1:3.

A pressure of 200 atmospheres is used, along with an iron catalyst to speed up the reaction. A higher pressure would be beneficial, but high pressure equipment is expensive to build, run and maintain, so again, a compromise pressure is used.

The reaction is a **continuous process**. After reacting, the mixture of gases is cooled to –33°C, the point at which ammonia is a liquid, and it is poured off. In this way, the unused nitrogen and hydrogen are recycled. The yield in this reaction is about 10%.

Nitric acid

We now have ammonia from the Haber process, but it is still not a nitrate, which can be used as a fertiliser. Nitrates can be made by reacting things with nitric acid, so it would be a good idea to convert ammonia to nitric acid.

1. Ammonia reacts with air to form nitrogen monoxide, a colourless gas. The reaction is speeded up by passing it over a platinum/rhodium catalyst and it is exothermic, so after starting it off at 900°C it continues by itself. The excess heat is recycled and used in the Haber process.

$$4NH_3 + 5O_2 \rightarrow 4NO + 6H_2O$$

2. Nitrogen monoxide reacts spontaneously with oxygen in the air to form nitrogen dioxide, a brown gas.

$$2NO + O_2 \rightarrow 2NO_2$$

3. After cooling, nitrogen dioxide is mixed with more air and passed up an absorber against the flow of water. It reacts to form nitric acid.

$$4NO_2 + O_2 + 2H_2O \rightarrow 4HNO_3$$

(Notice that in the above process, the only raw materials are air and water.)

The nitric acid produced can be used to make fertilisers, explosives and nylon. It can also be used to etch metals and to refine precious metals.

Fertilisers

Ammonia can be reacted with nitric acid to make ammonium nitrate – a good fertiliser because it contains a double dose of nitrogen, one in the cation and one in the anion:

$$NH_3 + HNO_3 \rightarrow NH_4NO_3$$

(Haber plants often make nitric acid and ammonia too. They are positioned near the raw materials (OK, it is not a difficult task to situate it near some air!), near ports for phosphate rock imports and near transport routes to distribute the product.)

Sulphuric acid

Sulphuric acid is produced by the **Contact process**. The raw materials are sulphur, water and air.

(Contact plants are positioned near to ports as sulphur is imported on boats. They must also be near a good transport system and near a good supply of water.)

1. Initially, sulphur is oxidised, to form sulphur dioxide.

$$S + O_2 \rightarrow SO_2$$

2. The sulphur dioxide is mixed with air and reacted with the oxygen to form sulphur trioxide. This reaction is reversible and highly exothermic. A vanadium(v) oxide catalyst is used in 'beds'. The mixture of gases is passed through several beds of the catalyst and cooled between each. A temperature of 450°C is used to increase the rate of reaction. Although a high pressure would be beneficial, a pressure of between 1 and 2 atmospheres yields over 90% sulphur trioxide, so it is not economical to spend more on high pressure equipment.

$$2SO_2 + O_2 \rightleftharpoons 2SO_3$$

3. If the sulphur trioxide were dissolved directly into water, acidic fumes would be produced in a highly exothermic reaction. This is very dangerous. In practice, it is added to concentrated sulphuric acid, which has a high boiling point, producing **oleum**. Oleum is added to water to produce 98% acid.

$$SO_3 + H_2SO_4 \rightarrow H_2S_2O_7$$

$$H_2S_2O_7 + H_2O \rightarrow 2H_2SO_4$$

> *(This whole process involves exothermic reactions. The excess heat is used to make steam and generate electricity, which is used to generate electricity for the process and to sell to electricity companies. It is therefore quite cheap to run a Contact plant as there is no additional cost to keep heating the raw materials. The only major costs are the sulphur and the labour.)*

Sulphuric acid is used in car batteries, to make detergents and to make fertilisers.

Concentrated sulphuric acid

- Concentrated sulphuric acid reacts violently and exothermically with water. To dilute it, add the acid to water, *not* water to acid.
- It is a dehydrating agent, taking hydrogen and oxygen from substances in the ratio of 2:1. It can dehydrate blue copper sulphate, making white anhydrous copper sulphate:

$$CuSO_4 \cdot 5H_2O \rightarrow CuSO_4 + 5H_2O$$

- In the same way, it will dehydrate sugar. It forms a disgusting black honeycomb of carbon in an exothermic reaction (ask your chemistry teacher to demonstrate it):

$$C_6H_{12}O_6 \rightarrow 6C + 6H_2O$$

The chlor-alkali industry

The sea is full of sodium chloride. Concentrated sodium chloride solution (brine) is electrolysed (see p. 52), to obtain **chlorine** in a very neat process. At the cathode, hydrogen ions from the water are reduced and hydrogen gas is formed. At the anode, chloride ions are oxidised to form chlorine gas:

$$2H^+ + 2e^- \rightarrow H_2$$

$$2Cl^- \rightarrow Cl_2 + 2e^-$$

This leaves OH⁻ ions and Na⁺ ions behind in the water, so the solution turns into good old **sodium hydroxide** – a very commonly used alkali. The products of this process have many uses.

- Sodium hydroxide is used in the manufacture of soap, paper, ceramics and oven cleaners.
- The hydrogen produced may be used in the Haber process or to make margarine.
- Chlorine may be dissolved in water to make bleach. Bleach is usually made by reacting chlorine with sodium hydroxide solution:

$$Cl_2 + 2NaOH \rightarrow NaOCl + NaCl + H_2O$$

- Chlorine can be used to kill bacteria or to make PVC (see p. 62).
- Silver chloride reacts to light and is used to make photographic paper.

Limestone

Limestone is mainly composed of calcium carbonate. It has many uses.

- It reacts with acids, so can be used to neutralise acidity in soil. It is insoluble, so adding too much limestone will not cause any harm. It will actually help neutralise any further acidity which arises:

$$CaCO_3 + 2H^+ \rightarrow Ca^{2+} + H_2O + CO_2$$

- It thermally decomposes to calcium oxide (**quicklime**) and carbon dioxide:

$$CaCO_3 \rightleftharpoons CaO + CO_2$$

This is used in industrial processes such as extraction of iron in blast furnaces (see p. 68).

- When water is added to quicklime it forms calcium hydroxide (**slaked lime**), which is also used to reduce acidity in soil:

$$CaO + H_2O \rightleftharpoons Ca(OH)_2$$

- Calcium hydroxide solution is also known as **lime water** and is used to test for the presence of carbon dioxide.

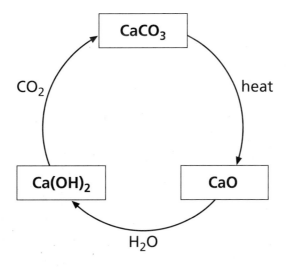

A cycle of reactions of calcium compounds

- Limestone is also used in the manufacture of **cement**. It is mixed with powdered clay and roasted in a rotary kiln. The solid clinker formed is ground up and the powder produced is called cement. When mixed with water, sand and crushed rock, a slow chemical reaction makes it harden into **concrete**.
- Glass is made by heating limestone with sand (and a little sodium carbonate):

$$CaCO_3 + SiO_2 \rightarrow CaSiO_3 + CO_2$$

Example questions

13.1 In the manufacture of aluminium, which electrode must be replaced regularly and why?

13.2 Outline and give the name of the process which is used to purify iron.

13.3 Suggest why magnesium blocks are attached to underwater pipes.

13.4 Write an ionic half equation for what happens at the cathode in the electrolysis of copper sulphate solution.

13.5 Give two reasons why it is important to produce ammonia, and give two uses for it.

13.6 Why is ammonium nitrate a good fertiliser?

13.7 Why is it dangerous to add sulphur trioxide to water?

13.8 What makes the production of chlorine from brine such a useful process?

13.9 Use the Appendix to find out the test for chlorine gas.

calculations

When chemists aren't busy mixing reactants together and classifying materials, it's likely that they're doing calculations. In GCSE chemistry, calculations are quite easy. They usually involve addition, subtraction, multiplication and division, with whole number results. If you remember just a few simple steps every time you do a chemical calculation, you can't go far wrong.

1. Write a *balanced* equation for the reaction. Always check you have written the correct formulae of compounds. Although they are usually given, it is a good idea to know them. Also, precipitation reactions are usually easier to represent as ionic equations. For example:

$$Ca^{2+}(aq) + SO_4{}^{2-}(aq) \rightarrow CaSO_4(s)$$

2. From the information you are given, work out the numbers of moles of the relevant substances. Remember to take into account the ratios of reactants and products.

3. When you know the number of moles of the substance in question, you can convert it to other units.

Moles

In chemistry, a **mole** is not actually a cute furry little animal that lives underground. It is a number, just like π. A mole could be 10 or 45 or any number. But, in fact, it is about 6×10^{23} molecules or atoms, **Avogadro's constant**. Oh, and chemists are quite fond of abbreviating things. Millilitres become ml, kilograms become kg and moles, well, they become mol.

Anyway, what does Avogadro's constant mean? Why is a mole 6×10^{23} molecules or atoms? Well, if you take 6×10^{23} atoms of an element (1 mole of atoms) and weigh it, you will get a number in grams. It just so happens that 1 mole of hydrogen atoms weigh 1 g. Note that 1 mole of hydrogen *molecules* (H_2, as it naturally occurs) weighs 2 g. One mole of helium atoms weigh 4 g. Strangely enough, this is the same as the **relative atomic mass** (A_r)!

But what about elements with isotopes? Chlorine has two isotopes, one with a mass of 35 and the other with a mass of 37. Do we quote the relative atomic mass of chlorine as 35 or 37. Well, it is neither. The ratio of chlorine 35 to chlorine 37 is 3:1, so an average is taken, taking into account the proportions of each isotope. So the relative atomic mass of chlorine works out at 35.5. For relative atomic mass, note that no units are given because the numbers are just relative to each other (and just happen to be the mass of 1 mole).

So, say you know that the relative atomic mass of carbon is 12 and that of oxygen is 16, and you want to find the **relative molecular mass** (M_r) of carbon dioxide. You know the formula of carbon dioxide is CO_2, so to work out its relative molecular mass, you just add the relative atomic masses of each of the atoms. There is 1 carbon atom and 2 oxygen atoms, so the relative molecular mass of CO_2 is $12 + (2 \times 16) = 44$. This means that the mass of 1 mole of carbon dioxide is 44 g.

From this, you can work out the **percentage** of carbon in carbon dioxide by mass. In 44 g of CO_2, there are 12 g of carbon. So, the percentage is given by:

$$\frac{mass}{relative\ molecular\ mass} \times 100 = \frac{12}{44} \times 100$$

$$= 27.3\%$$

In the same way that given the number of moles of something you can work out the mass of it, well if you are given the mass of something you can work out the number of moles of it. For example, the M_r of calcium carbonate is 100 ($40 + 12 + 16 \times 3$). This means that the mass of 1 mole of $CaCO_3 = 100$ g. Using the formula:

$$number\ of\ moles = \frac{mass}{mass\ of\ 1\ mole}$$

we can work out how many moles are in 42 g of $CaCO_3$:

$$number\ of\ moles = \frac{42}{100}$$

$$= 0.42\ mol$$

The above formula is the golden formula of chemical calculations, which must be learned as it will be used all the time. You can also rearrange it so that the mass can be found from the number of moles and the M_r or the M_r can be found from the number of moles and the mass.

Using moles with chemical equations

Consider the following question:

What mass of sodium oxide is formed when 46 g of sodium are burned in excess air?

• The first thing to do is write a balanced chemical equation:

$4Na + O_2 \rightarrow 2Na_2O$

(It is useful to leave a gap below the equation to write down the information you have been given.)

- Next work out the number of moles of whatever is needed, because moles can be converted to and from many other units. So, the number of moles of sodium used must be worked out:

$$\text{number of moles} = \frac{\text{mass}}{\text{mass of 1 mole}} = \frac{46}{23} = \textbf{2 mol}$$

- It is then useful to write your new information below the equation. Since for every 4 moles of sodium used, 2 moles of sodium oxide are produced, then the ratio of sodium to sodium oxide is 2:1. This means that if 2 moles of sodium are used, half the number of moles of sodium oxide are produced (i.e. 1 mole of Na_2O):

$4Na + O_2 \rightarrow 2Na_2O$

46 g   ?

2 mol   1 mol

- So, 1 mole of sodium oxide has a mass of $23 \times 2 + 16 = \textbf{62 g}$.

It's that simple! As long as you work to moles from the information given in the question, and from there, using the ratios of substances, work towards the answer – you can't go wrong.

Empirical formula

Taking the earlier example of carbon dioxide, you worked out that it is made up of 1 mole of carbon atoms and 2 moles of oxygen atoms, hence CO_2. So, the ratio of carbon to oxygen is 1:2. Therefore, knowing the ratios of the atoms making up a molecule, you can work out the formula of it. For example, if the ratio of moles in a compound containing iron and oxygen is 2 : 3 respectively, the formula must be Fe_2O_3.

The **empirical formula** of a molecule is the simplest ratio of atoms. This means that although ethane is C_2H_6, the simplest ratio is 1:3, so the empirical formula is CH_3. The **molecular formula** takes into account the actual numbers of atoms, so the molecular formula of ethane is C_2H_6.

This means that you now know three types of formula:

| CH_3 | C_2H_6 | structural formula |
| empirical formula | molecular formula | structural formula |

Different formulae for ethane

Exam questions will tell you the masses of each atom in a compound and you must work out the number of moles of the atoms, and from that their simplest ratio, so you can work out the empirical formula. For example, a typical question might be:

> *An oxide of phosphorus was found to have 3.10 g of phosphorus and 4 g of oxygen. Find its empirical formula.*

- Since you have been given the masses of the constituents of phosphorus and oxygen, you can work out the numbers of moles:

$$\text{number of moles} = \frac{\text{mass}}{\text{mass of 1 mole}}$$

Therefore, for phosphorus: and for oxygen:

$$\text{number of moles} = \frac{3.1}{31} = \textbf{0.1 mol} \qquad \text{number of moles} = \frac{4}{16} = \textbf{0.25 mol}$$

- The ratio of phosphorus to oxygen is 0.1 : 0.25

  If the ratio is multiplied by 20 to get the simplest whole number ratio, it becomes 2:5.

- Therefore, the empirical formula is **P_2O_5**.

Some exam questions will give the percentages of each element or atom by mass. In this case, just pretend there are 100 g. So, if a compound contains 60% magnesium and 40% oxygen, just assume that it contains 60 g of magnesium and 40 g of oxygen.

Gases

Whatever the gas, **1 mole of any gas occupies 24 litres at room temperature and pressure (r.t.p)**. You'll be glad to know that this makes for really easy calculations!

> *(By the way, litres and dm³ (decimetres cubed) are the same volume, just a different way of saying it.)*

Look again at the question about the oxidation of sodium:

$$4Na + O_2 \rightarrow 2Na_2O$$

You can work out how many litres of oxygen are required. Since you worked out before that 2 moles of sodium were used, you can now determine the volume of oxygen used:

The ratio of sodium to oxygen is 4 : 1, so the number of moles of oxygen is one quarter of the number of moles of sodium = 0.5 mol. Since 1 mole of any gas occupies 24 litres at r.t.p. 0.5 moles of oxygen = 0.5 × 24 = **12 litres**.

Electrolysis

When doing calculations for electrolysis, you have to be a bit careful when dealing with ionic half equations.

The half equations for the electrolysis of potassium chloride are:

At the cathode: $K^+ + e^- \rightarrow K$

At the anode: $2Cl^- \rightarrow Cl_2 + 2e^-$

This is where you have to be careful. One mole of electrons is required to discharge 1 mole of potassium atoms. One mole of electrons will also be discharged from 1 mole of chloride ions, but because chlorine is diatomic, one mole of electrons will be discharged from only half a mole of chlorine gas molecules. Therefore if 1 mole of potassium is formed, half a mole of chlorine gas (Cl_2) is formed. The amount of chlorine can be given as a mass *or* as the volume at r.t.p.

Calculating concentrations of solutions

The concentration of a solution is given in moles of solute per litre (dm^3) of solvent. The concentration is sometimes referred to as the **molarity**. A solution that contains 1 mole per litre is 1 molar (1 M). For a solution of 5 moles per litre, it is 5 molar (5 M). You only have to know 1 equation to tackle any question about solutions:

number of moles of solute = volume in litres $\times$ concentration.

For example, if you are asked:

What is the concentration of the hydrochloric acid produced if 7.3 g of hydrogen chloride are dissolved in 250 cm³ of water?

- It is always a good idea to convert everything to the required units at the beginning of the answer:

  250 cm³ = 0.25 litres.

  If 1 mole of HCl = 36.5 g, then 7.3 g = 0.2 mol.

- concentration = $\dfrac{\text{moles}}{\text{volume}}$

  $\therefore$ concentration = $\dfrac{0.2}{0.25}$ = **0.8 mol/l**

  *(Note that concentration can be written in several different ways which mean the same thing. The above value of 0.8 mol/l could be written as **0.8 mol l⁻¹ or 0.8 mol dm⁻³**.)*

Titration

You have probably seen or done a titration practical to find the molarity of an acid or alkali. For GCSE, you should be able to calculate the molarity of an acid or alkali based on the information given. For example, a typical question may be:

Calculate the molarity of sulphuric acid solution, if exactly 25 cm³ react with exactly 30 cm³ of 2.0 M sodium hydroxide.

- The first thing to do is write the equation. It is often easier to leave three lines under the equation, one for moles, one for volume and one for concentration:

$H_2SO_4 + 2NaOH \rightarrow Na_2SO_4 + 2H_2O$

Moles	**0.030 moles**	**0.060 moles**
Volume	0.025 litres	0.030 litres
Conc.	?	2.0 mol/l

- Next, write down the information given in the question in the appropriate spaces under the equation (see above) – remembering to convert the measurements to the appropriate units. For example, the volumes in cm³ are better off being divided by 1000 to convert them to litres.

- The number of moles of NaOH needs to be found so that the number of moles of sulphuric acid can be worked out from the ratios:

moles = conc. × volume = 0.03×2 = **0.06 moles**
(write this in the appropriate space).

- The ratio, by moles, of acid to NaOH = 1:2, so **0.03 moles** of H_2SO_4 are used (write this in the appropriate space).

- You can now work out the concentration of the acid:

$$\text{concentration} = \frac{\text{moles}}{\text{volume}}$$

$$\therefore \text{concentration} = \frac{0.03}{0.025} = \textbf{1.2 M}$$

Example questions

14.1 Write the number of moles of the following, giving answers to 3 significant figures where necessary:

(a) 13 g of potassium
(b) 16 g of oxygen gas
(c) 5 litres of helium gas
(d) 18 tonnes of magnesium

14.2 An organic compound contains 40.0% carbon, 6.67% hydrogen and 53.3% oxygen by mass. It has a relative molecular mass of 180.

(a) Find the numbers of moles of each element present.
(b) Hence, find the empirical formula of the compound.
(c) Using information about the relative molecular mass, find the molecular formula of the compound.

14.3 What volume of nitrogen is required to form 17 g of ammonia gas in the Haber process at r.t.p.?

14.4 In the electrolysis of aluminium oxide, what mass of aluminium is obtained when 36 litres of oxygen are produced?

14.5 What volume of 0.6 M nitric acid is required to neutralise 25 cm³ of 1 M potassium hydroxide?

the atmosphere

You are expected to know a little about the Earth's atmosphere and how it has changed over vast periods of time. The easiest way to learn it is from a chain of events.

A brief history

1. The first few billion years after the Earth formed, it was cooling down. This cooling meant intense volcanic eruptions, spewing out carbon dioxide, water vapour and a little methane and ammonia.

2. As the Earth cooled further, the water formed vast oceans. Basic green plant life then evolved.

3. Green plants photosynthesised, producing oxygen from carbon dioxide, thus reducing the levels of carbon dioxide and introducing oxygen into the atmosphere. Oxygen was initially a pollutant, as a by-product of photosynthesis.

4. Many people are surprised to hear that oxygen was actually very poisonous to this early plant life. A large amount died because it could not tolerate the oxygen, and new tolerant species evolved.

5. Then, organisms evolved through natural selection that could use oxygen and convert it to carbon dioxide (aerobic respiration), by eating the plants.

6. Gradually, the carbon from carbon dioxide became locked up as sedimentary rocks, carbonates and in life (all life is carbon-based).

7. Ammonia in the atmosphere reacted with oxygen to form nitrogen. Methane formed water and carbon dioxide.

8. Ozone formed in the upper atmosphere due to the action of sunlight on the oxygen.

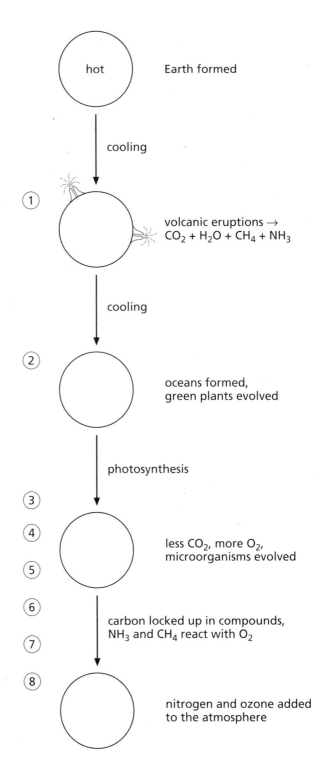

Earth formed — hot

cooling

① volcanic eruptions →
$CO_2 + H_2O + CH_4 + NH_3$

cooling

② oceans formed,
green plants evolved

photosynthesis

③
④ less CO_2, more O_2,
⑤ microorganisms evolved
⑥
carbon locked up in compounds,
⑦ NH_3 and CH_4 react with O_2
⑧
nitrogen and ozone added
to the atmosphere

Composition of the atmosphere

The atmosphere has since stabilised, so now there is little change in the content of the atmosphere. Green plants produce oxygen from carbon dioxide at the same rate as it is respired and converted back to carbon dioxide, so there is constantly about 21% oxygen and 0.04% carbon dioxide. 78% of the atmosphere is nitrogen and 1% is argon, a noble gas used in light bulbs (yes, it does add up to over 100%, but it is only approximate!).

Air pollution

There is concern about increasing levels of carbon dioxide, a greenhouse gas (see p. 56). It is thought to be contributing to global warming. Burning fossil fuels (which contain carbon from ancient life) increases the amount of carbon dioxide in the atmosphere. This acts like the glass in a greenhouse, keeping the Earth warm.

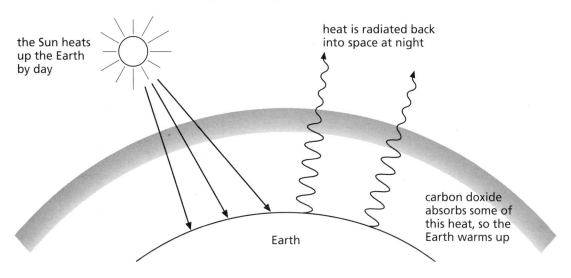

The greenhouse effect

Green plants use carbon dioxide in photosynthesis and sea water absorbs carbon dioxide, but not fast enough to cope with the increasing levels in the atmosphere.

Example questions

15.1 Which natural processes are responsible for balancing the amounts of carbon dioxide and oxygen in the atmosphere?

15.2 Explain why increasing levels of carbon dioxide could be blamed for the rise in sea levels.

rocks and tectonics

The GCSE syllabus for chemistry includes some geography. Isn't there enough chemistry to fill a syllabus or something? Well, it's there, so you better learn it!

When the Earth had just been formed, it was a molten mass. It slowly cooled and the surface solidified, forming the **crust**. Denser materials sank deeper into the **core**. The crust floats on a layer of magma called the **mantle**. This is liquid rock which is viscous and does not flow easily.

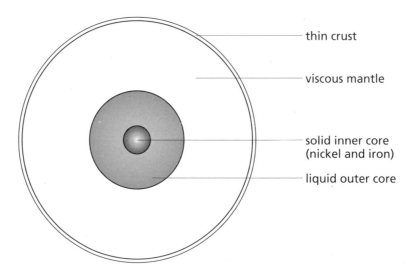

Cross-section through the Earth

The crust is made of several types of rock – igneous, sedimentary and metamorphic. Much like all natural substances, there is a rock cycle, showing how they are converted from one form to another.

Types of rock

Igneous rocks

Deep within the core of the Earth, radioactive substances decay and give out huge amounts of heat. This heat melts the lower part of the crust and the upper part of the mantle. This melted material is **magma**. Igneous rocks are formed when magma cools and solidifies. They are crystalline in structure and can be one of two types.

- **Intrusive** igneous rocks are formed when molten magma is forced into the Earth's crust. The Earth's crust is warm, so the magma cools slowly. This allows the ions to line themselves up over a long period of time, so large crystals form. An example of an extrusive igneous rock is granite.
- **Extrusive** igneous rocks are formed when magma reaches the Earth's surface (perhaps through a volcanic eruption). Magma on the Earth's surface is called **lava**. Since the Earth's surface is much cooler than the crust, the lava cools much more quickly so very small crystals form. An example of an extrusive rock is basalt.

Rocks made up of randomly interlocking crystals, with any variety of minerals, are likely to be igneous.

Sedimentary rocks

Sedimentary rocks are formed by layers of small grains, for example of sand, which build up over a large period of time and are compressed so they cement together. They are soft because these grains can easily be separated. Layers of sedimentary rocks are often found tilted, folded, fractured (cracked down the middle) and even upside down. Movement caused by huge forces in the Earth's crust are responsible for this.

Examples of sedimentary rocks are mudstones, sandstones and limestones composed of calcium carbonate, which are made from a build-up of the remains of the shells of dead organisms.

Sedimentary rocks can contain fossils. Sediments may be laid down on top of the bones of dead organisms. The bones slowly decay and sediment replaces the bone, which is compressed and preserved in the rock. A rock can be dated by observing the fossils found in it and relating these to the era in which the particular organisms lived.

Carbonate rocks can move deep within the Earth and decompose upon heating, letting out carbon dioxide. The carbon dioxide then returns to the atmosphere via volcanoes.

Metamorphic rocks

Metamorphic rocks were made and still are being made deep within the roots of mountains. They arise due to high temperatures and pressures associated with the forces present when mountains are forming. Tectonic activity (more on this later) can bury rocks deep within the Earth's crust, where they are subjected to high temperatures and pressures from the mass of rock above and side pressures from the processes of mountain building. They do not melt because of the high pressure, but their structure and therefore texture does change, and they become metamorphic rocks.

When the sedimentary rock mudstone is subjected to these forces, it becomes slate. Limestone becomes marble. These metamorphic rocks have a very high density and the crystal grains all face one direction, making them seem layered. Unlike igneous rocks, which have randomly interlocking crystals, metamorphic rocks have interlocking **bands** of crystals, such as schist.

> *(AQA: NEAB candidates: You should be able to use the data book to identify rock types.)*

Weathering

Weathering is loosely described as the action of wind, rain and frost on rocks. It gradually breaks rocks down. Heating and cooling rocks will also weather them, as will gases in the atmosphere, which react with them over periods of time. You know that hard water is made when water and carbon dioxide react with limestone (see p. 46). This is an example of weathering. Over millions of years, rocks are worn down and broken into smaller pieces. Tiny fragments of rocks mix with dead plants and animals. The result is **soil** (humus).

Another form of weathering is in rivers. Running rivers carry small particles with them. The faster the river, the larger the particles it can carry. These particles rub against rocks in the bank and chip pieces off (**erosion**). When the river slows it cannot hold as much solid matter, so the pieces of rock drop to the bed and form a sediment. Can you guess what happens next? Yes, you guessed it… millions of years, intense pressure squeezing out the water, and *voila* – sedimentary rocks!

The rock cycle

Just like water, carbon and old bottles, rocks too are recycled. The diagram below illustrates the rock cycle. Let's start from the beginning.

1. Rocks are weathered and eroded.
2. The sediments produced are washed into rivers by rain water and deposited in the sea, where they are buried and cemented, forming sedimentary rocks.
3. These may be carried to the surface, where the cycle repeats itself or they could be buried deeper.
4. When buried deeper, they are subjected to high temperatures and pressures and metamorphic rocks are made, which could be slowly lifted to the surface, such as when mountains are formed.
5. Alternatively, they can get buried even deeper and melt again, making magma.
6. The magma can then become either extrusive or intrusive igneous rock, depending of whether it cools at the Earth's surface or within the crust.

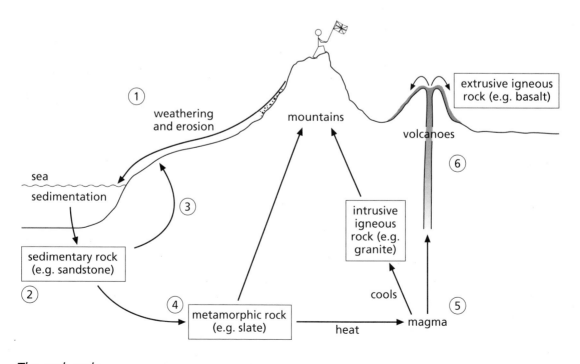

The rock cycle

Tectonics

As you now know, the Earth has a thin crust floating on a **viscous** mantle. The core is made of nickel and iron. The outer part of the core is liquid due to the great heat from radioactive decay, but the pressure of the inner core is so great that it is solid.

The Earth's crust is made of several large interlocking sections or **plates**. These move slowly and, over millions of years, form mountain ranges and oceans. The movement of the plates is caused by convection currents of magma. Deep magma is heated, rises, moves along a bit, then sinks again, as shown in the diagram.

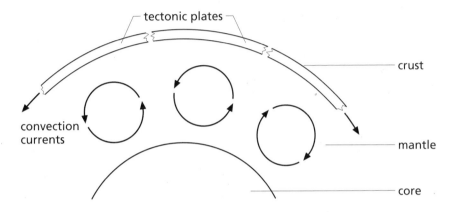

Convection currents cause tectonic plates to move

At one time, the Earth was just one huge land mass with an ocean surrounding it (a big island). It cracked into several large pieces (tectonic plates), which float on the mantle and move.

> *(Originally, it was believed that the separate land masses formed as the Earth was cooling and shrinking.)*

There are three ways tectonic plates can interact.

- **Sliding past**
  Tectonic plates can slide past each other, resulting in **faults**. For example, along the Californian coast, the plates are sliding past each other sideways. The San Andreas Fault moves at the rate of about 1 cm each year. Sometimes the plates get stuck until enough pressure builds up for them to jolt back into position. This is an **earthquake**.

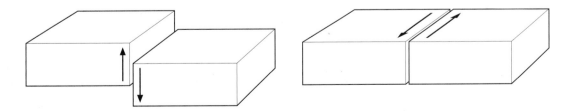

Plates can slide past each other

- **Moving towards**
  Plates can be pushed together. Oceanic plates are thinner than continental (land) plates, but denser, so they are tucked under the continental plates. The sinking

oceanic plates melt in the magma, whilst the continental plates are forced up. At the point where the oceanic plate is sinking, ocean trenches may form, like the Marianas Trench in the Pacific Ocean. The collision makes the crust crack (faulting) and fold up into mountain ranges. The magma may rise through weakened crust to form **volcanos**. The best examples of this type of **destructive** plate movement are along the western edge of South America.

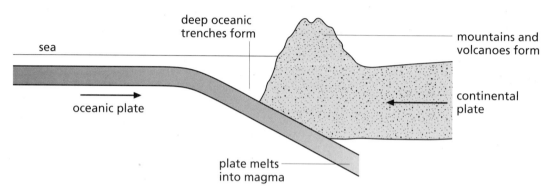

Plates can move towards each other

- **Moving apart**
  If plates move apart, magma rises up and solidifies to fill the gap, producing new basaltic oceanic crust. This is called **sea floor spreading** and is a **constructive** fault. It happens along oceanic ridges, including the Mid-Atlantic ridge.

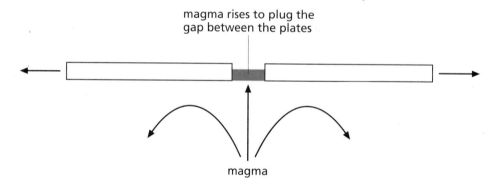

Plates can move away from each other

Materials in magma containing iron align themselves according to the Earth's magnetic field. When the magma solidifies, these minerals stay aligned the same way. There is evidence that the poles have switched several times in history because as you dig deeper in the crust, the minerals are lined up in layers facing opposite directions.

Example questions

16.1 Explain why pebbles at the beach are rounded, whereas pebbles in rivers are not.

16.2 Can fossils form in igneous rocks? Explain your answer.

16.3 Suggest why tectonic plates moving apart are called constructive faults.

16.4 Why is the inner core of the Earth solid?

answers to example questions

topic one

1.1

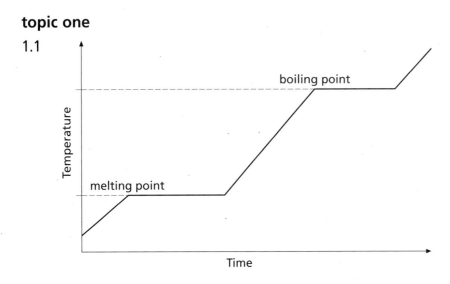

1.2 The particles in gases have more energy and move about more freely than in solids. This makes them move faster and they are further away from each other, so they take up more room.

1.3

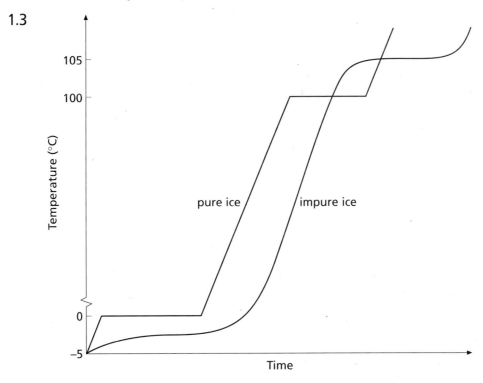

topic two

2.1 (a) Compound
(b) Element
(c) Mixture

2.2 (a) Add water to the mixture to make the salt dissolve, then filter it. The salt solution will have passed through the filter paper and collected in a beaker. This can be evaporated to obtain salt crystals. The residue of pepper should be washed to get rid of any salt remaining and then dried.

(b) The air could be cooled to the boiling point of oxygen (–183°C) and fractionally distilled.

(c) A sample of blood can be centrifuged, throwing the solid portion to the base of a test tube, with the liquid plasma on top.

2.3 Green (blue and yellow dyes are present).

topic three

3.1 Sodium will react more violently with water. The reactivity will be determined by how easily the outer electron can be lost – the easier it is for the metal to lose the electron, the more reactive it is. The outer electron of sodium is further from the nucleus than in lithium, and there are more energy levels of electrons screening the attraction of the outer electron to the nucleus. Therefore the outer electron will be lost more easily – sodium will be more active than lithium.

3.2 If stored in air, they will react with the oxygen in it and may ignite. Storing them under oil protects them from the air.

3.3 A brown liquid (bromine) is produced because the chlorine displaces the bromide ion.

3.4 No, because bromine is less reactive than chlorine so cannot displace the chloride ion.

topic four

4.1 24 – 12 = 12 neutrons

4.2 (a) 2,8,6
(b) 2,8,8,1
(c) 2,8
(d) 2,8

4.3 H_2O – deuterium is just an isotope of hydrogen, so it has the same chemical properties.

4.4 (a) $NaNO_3$
(b) $CaCl_2$
(c) SO_2
(d) H_2SO_4

4.5 (a) Potassium nitrate
(b) Lithium sulphate
(c) Ammonia (nitrogen hydride)
(d) Nitric acid (hydrogen nitrate)

4.6 Sodium oxide is made of a metal and a non-metal, so it is ionically bonded, with strong electrostatic forces between ions. Sulphur dioxide is made up of two non-metals, so it has strong covalent bonds within the molecules but weak van der Waals forces between molecules, therefore it will melt more easily.

4.7 (a) Isotopes of an element have the same number of protons and electrons, but a different number of neutrons.

(b) Allotropes of an element have different molecular structures and therefore different physical properties (such as graphite and diamond, which are allotropes of carbon with very different characteristics).

(c) This is a covalent molecule which can potentially continue forever, with strong covalent bonds between all atoms.

(d) This is a charged particle.

topic five

5.1 React it with water, steam and a dilute acid. The more reactive the metal, the more violent the reaction with water, steam and acid (if any happens at all). Next, perform the same test on aluminium, magnesium and zinc and compare them with the reactivity of metal X.

5.2 It is a redox reaction, the aluminium being oxidised and the iron being reduced.

5.3 Since hydrogen is more reactive than copper, it will displace the copper ion from the copper oxide, thus forming water and copper.

topic six

6.1 (a) The carbonate was in larger pieces in experiment 2, so there was less surface with which acid particles could collide and react. Hence, the reaction was slower.

(b)

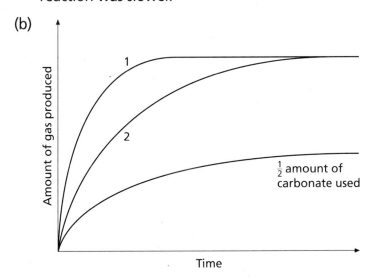

topic seven

7.1 (a) Red
(b) Green
(c) Purple
(d) Orange
(e) Blue

7.2 (a) Reaction of hydrochloric acid and zinc metal.
   (b) Precipitation (silver chloride is insoluble). In the lab, this can be prepared by reacting hydrochloric acid with silver nitrate.
   (c) Titration, perhaps of potassium hydroxide with hydrogen iodide.
   (d) Direct combination of iron and chlorine.

7.3 Direct synthesis is preferred over acid/alkali reaction if an anhydrous salt is required or if the reaction is easier (or often cheaper in industry). If this is not possible, but you want to obtain an anhydrous salt, a hydrated salt can be dehydrated, perhaps by using concentrated sulphuric acid.

topic eight

8.1 Respiration is exothermic. The more we work, the more we respire and therefore the more heat we produce.

8.2 (a) $CH_4 + 2O_2 \rightarrow CO_2 + 2H_2O$

- First, bonds in reactants are broken, requiring energy:

  4 C—H bonds in methane are broken = $435 \times 4 = 1740$ kJ
  2 O=O bonds in oxygen are broken = $397 \times 2 = 794$ kJ

  Total energy required = $1740 + 794 = 2534$ kJ

- Then, energy is released as new bonds are formed:

  2 C=O bonds are formed in carbon dioxide = $803 \times 2 = 1606$ kJ
  4 O—H bonds are formed in the 2 moles of water produced = 464×4
  = 1856 kJ

  Total energy released = $1856 + 1606 = 3462$ kJ

- Energy given out = $3462 - 2534 = $ **928 kJ per mole**

(b)

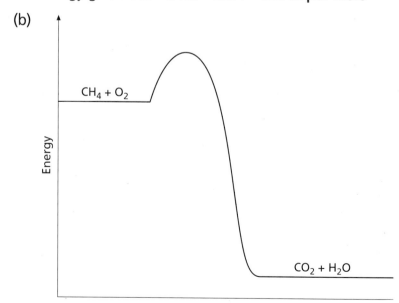

topic nine

9.1 The equipment required to achieve a higher pressure than 200 atm is extremely expensive to buy and maintain, so it is uneconomical to use.

9.2 If the temperature is much lower, the reaction would occur much more slowly, so the yield will decrease in a given time. It is also true that transition metal catalysts only start working at temperature around 450°C.

topic ten

10.1 A white precipitate of calcium carbonate forms, because the calcium hydrogen carbonate thermally decomposes:

$$Ca(HCO_3)_2(aq) \rightarrow CaCO_3(s) + H_2O(l) + CO_2(aq)$$

10.2 It kills bacteria in the water, which may cause disease. The concentration of chlorine in swimming pools is greater than in drinking water so potentially disease-causing bacteria are very quickly killed before they can be ingested by another person.

10.3 Concentrated sodium chloride solution can be poured through the pipe. Since NaCl solution contains Na^+ ions, it can 'refill' the ion exchanger.

10.4 10 g (60 – 20 = 40 g in 100 cm^3 of water ∴ 40 ÷ 4 = 10 g in 25 cm^3)

topic eleven

11.1 (a) $Cu^{2+}(aq) + 2e^- \rightarrow Cu(s)$
 (b) $2H^+(aq) + 2e^- \rightarrow H_2(g)$
 (c) $Al^{3+}(aq) + 3e^- \rightarrow Al(s)$

11.2 Zinc is more reactive than iron (steel). It will therefore react with oxygen in preference to the iron and be oxidised instead of it.

11.3 Nothing. Sulphur dioxide is a covalent molecule, therefore it does not exist as ions which are free to move about.

topic twelve

12.1 1 2 3

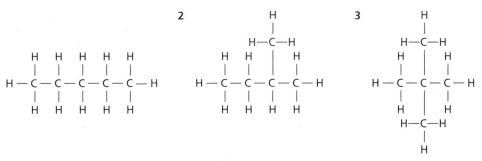

12.2 Complete: $CH_4 + 2O_2 \rightarrow CO_2 + 2H_2O$

 Incomplete: $2CH_4 + 3O_2 \rightarrow 2CO + 4H_2O$ or $CH_4 + O_2 \rightarrow C + 2H_2O$

12.3 Any three fractions from the table on p. 57.

12.4 Isomer A is octane. It has a higher boiling point because it is not branched, so there is more surface area to attract other molecules.

12.5

ethene   poly(ethene)

Conditions required are high pressure and a catalyst. It is an example of addition polymerisation.

12.6 Hydration of ethene is more suitable to produce ethanol for medical use as it produces pure ethanol.

12.7 The ethanol in the wine reacts with oxygen, forming ethanoic acid. Acids generally taste sour. (Ethanoic acid is actually vinegar.)

topic thirteen

13.1 The anode must be replaced regularly as oxygen is produced at it. At the high temperature, it reacts with the graphite electrode, producing carbon dioxide. This means the electrode wastes away.

13.2 The Basic Oxygen Process is used, in which oxygen is bubbled through the molten iron and calcium carbonate is added. The calcium carbonate decomposes to carbon dioxide and calcium oxide, a basic oxide. Meanwhile, non-metallic impurities such as sulphur and carbon react with the oxygen, forming acidic oxides. These are neutralised by the calcium oxide and float on the surface, to form slag, which is poured off.

13.3 Magnesium is more reactive than the metal of which the pipes are made. It will therefore react and corrode in preference to the metal of the pipe, prolonging the life of the pipe.

13.4 $Cu^{2+}(aq) + 2e^- \rightarrow Cu(s)$

13.5 Ammonia contains nitrogen, which is required in a combined form by all life to make essential proteins. It is used to make fertiliser and nitric acid.

13.6 It contains a 'double dose' of nitrogen. One dose is in the nitrate anion and there is some in the ammonium cation.

13.7 The reaction is highly exothermic, producing extremely dangerous acidic fumes.

13.8 Hydrochloric acid is made from the chlorine but, more importantly, large quantities of sodium hydroxide are also produced. This is an extremely widely used chemical.

13.9 Chlorine gas will bleach damp litmus paper.

topic fourteen

14.1 (a) A_r of K = 39

$$\text{no. of moles} = \frac{\text{mass}}{\text{mass of 1 mole}} = \frac{13}{39} = \frac{1}{3} \text{ mol or } \mathbf{0.333 \ mol}$$

(b) M_r of O_2 = 32

$$\text{moles} = \frac{16}{32} = \frac{1}{2} \text{ mol or } \mathbf{0.5 \ mol}$$

(c) 1 mole of any gas at r.t.p. = 24 litres

$$\therefore \text{ in 5 litres there are } \frac{5}{24} = \mathbf{0.208 \ mol}$$

(d) A_r of Mg = 24

18 tonnes = 18 000 000 g

$$\text{no. of moles} = \frac{18 \ 000 \ 000}{24} = \mathbf{750 \ 000 \ mol}$$

or

18 tonnes = 1.8×10^7 g

$$\text{no. of moles} = \frac{1.8 \times 10^7}{24} = 0.075 \times 10^7 = \mathbf{7.5 \times 10^5 \ mol}$$

14.2 (a) In 100 g: 40.0 g are C, A_r of C = 12
6.67 g are H, A_r of H = 1
53.3 g are O, A_r of O = 16

$$\text{no. of moles of } \mathbf{C} = \frac{40}{12} = \mathbf{3.33 \ mol}$$

$$\mathbf{H} = \frac{6.67}{1} = \mathbf{6.67 \ mol}$$

$$\mathbf{O} = \frac{53.3}{16} = \mathbf{3.33 \ mol}$$

(b)

element	C	H	O
ratio	3.33	6.67	3.33
whole no. ratio	1	2	1

$\therefore$ empirical formula = $\mathbf{CH_2O}$

(c) M_r of CH_2O = 30

If M_r of compound = 180, everything is scaled up by $\dfrac{180}{30} = 6$

$\therefore$ molecular formula = $\mathbf{C_6H_{12}O_6}$

14.3 $N_2 + 3H_2 \rightarrow 2NH_3$

17 g of NH_3 = 1 mol

ratio of N_2 to NH_3 = 1 : 2

∴ 0.5 mol of N_2 is required

If 1 mol = 24 l at r.t.p.

0.5 mol = **12 l**

14.4 $2Al_2O_3 \rightarrow 4Al + 3O_2$

36 l of $O_2 = \dfrac{36}{24} = 1.5$ mol

ratio of Al to O_2 = 4 : 3

∴ $\dfrac{4}{3} \times 1.5 = 2$ mol Al produced

M_r of Al = 27

∴ mass = 27 × 2 = **54 g**

14.5 $KOH + HNO_3 \rightarrow KNO_3 + H_2O$

mol.   0.025

vol.   25 cm³

conc.   1 M   0.6 M

no. of moles of KOH = conc. × vol. = 1 × 0.025

= **0.025 mol**

∴ 0.025 mol of HNO_3 is required

vol. = $\dfrac{\text{mol.}}{\text{conc.}} = \dfrac{0.025}{0.6} = 0.042$ l or **42 cm³**

topic fifteen

15.1 Photosynthesis produces the oxygen from carbon dioxide, and respiration converts the oxygen back to carbon dioxide.

15.2 Carbon dioxide is a 'greenhouse gas'. It is responsible for keeping heat in the atmosphere, so the atmospheric temperature is rising, and so could cause polar ice caps to melt and increase the level of the sea.

topic sixteen

16.1 In the seas, sharp-edged stones rub together, eroding the surfaces and making them smooth. They are deposited on the beach.

16.2 No. Fossils are made only when layers of sediment form over bones of dead animals. Igneous rocks are made from magma, not from sediment.

16.3 They allow more material to fill the gap they make, thus constructing more land.

16.4 It is under great pressure, that prevents it from melting.

appendices

Periodic table

Valencies of common ions

Electronic configurations

Reactivity series of metals

Tests for common ions

Tests for common gases

Some old favourites

Periodic table

						Mass number A	1							
							H							
					Proton number (Atomic number) Z		1							

1	2											3	4	5	6	7	0
																	4 He 2
7 Li 3	9 Be 4											11 B 5	12 C 6	14 N 7	16 O 8	19 F 9	20 Ne 10
23 Na 11	24 Mg 12											27 Al 13	28 Si 14	31 P 15	32 S 16	35 Cl 17	40 Ar 18
39 K 19	40 Ca 20	45 Sc 21	48 Ti 22	51 V 23	52 Cr 24	55 Mn 25	56 Fe 26	59 Co 27	59 Ni 28	64 Cu 29	65 Zn 30	70 Ga 31	73 Ge 32	75 As 33	79 Se 34	80 Br 35	84 Kr 36
85 Rb 37	88 Sr 38	89 Y 39	91 Zr 40	93 Nb 41	96 Mo 42	Tc 43	101 Ru 44	103 Rh 45	106 Pd 46	108 Ag 47	112 Cd 48	115 In 49	119 Sn 50	122 Sb 51	128 Te 52	127 I 53	131 Xe 54
133 Cs 55	137 Ba 56	139 La 57	178 Hf 72	181 Ta 73	184 W 74	186 Re 75	190 Os 76	192 Ir 77	195 Pt 78	197 Au 79	201 Hg 80	204 Tl 81	207 Pb 82	209 Bi 83	Po 84	At 85	Rn 86
Fr 87	226 Ra 88	227 Ac 89															

140 Ce 58	141 Pr 59	144 Nd 60	Pm 61	150 Sm 62	152 Eu 63	157 Gd 64	159 Tb 65	162 Dy 66	165 Ho 67	167 Er 68	169 Tm 69	173 Yb 70	175 Lu 71
232 Th 90	Pa 91	238 U 92	Np 93	Pu 94	Am 95	Cm 96	Bk 97	Cf 98	Es 99	Fm 100	Md 101	No 102	Lr 103

Valencies of common ions

Positive ions

Hydrogen	H^+
Sodium	Na^+
Silver	Ag^+
Potassium	K^+
Lithium	Li^+
Ammonium	NH_4^+
Barium	Ba^{2+}
Calcium	Ca^{2+}
Copper(II)	Cu^{2+}
Magnesium	Mg^{2+}
Zinc	Zn^{2+}
Lead	Pb^{2+}
Iron(II)	Fe^{2+}
Iron (III)	Fe^{3+}
Aluminium	Al^{3+}

Negative ions

Chloride	Cl^-
Bromide	Br^-
Fluoride	F^-
Iodide	I^-
Hydroxide	OH^-
Nitrate	NO_3^-
Oxide	O^{2-}
Sulphide	S^{2-}
Sulphate	SO_4^{2-}
Carbonate	CO_3^{2-}

Electronic configurations

Element	Electronic configuration
1 hydrogen	1
2 helium	2
3 lithium	2, 1
4 beryllium	2, 2
5 boron	2, 3
6 carbon	2, 4
7 nitrogen	2, 5
8 oxygen	2, 6
9 fluorine	2, 7
10 neon	2, 8
11 sodium	2, 8, 1
12 magnesium	2, 8, 2
13 aluminium	2, 8, 3
14 silicon	2, 8, 4
15 phosphorus	2, 8, 5
16 sulphur	2, 8, 6
17 chlorine	2, 8, 7
18 argon	2, 8, 8
19 potassium	2, 8, 8, 1
20 calcium	2, 8, 8, 2

Reactivity series of metals

Potassium	most reactive
Sodium	
Calcium	
Magnesium	
Aluminium	
Zinc	
Iron	
Tin	
Lead	
Copper	
Silver	
Gold	
Platinum	least reactive

Tests for common ions

Ion	*Test*
Chloride (Cl$^-$)	Add a few drops of nitric acid and then a few drops of silver nitrate solution. A white precipitate is formed.
Sulphate (SO$_4$$^{2-}$)	Add a few drops of nitric acid then a few drops of barium nitrate solution. A white precipitate is formed.
Carbonate (CO$_3$$^{2-}$)	Add dilute hydrochloric acid to the solid (or mix with the solution). Bubbles of gas are given off.
Iron (II) (Fe^{2+})	Add aqueous sodium hydroxide to the solution. A pale green jelly-like precipitate is formed.
Iron (III) (Fe^{3+})	Add aqueous sodium hydroxide to the solution. A brown jelly-like precipitate is formed.
Copper (II) (Cu^{2+})	Add aqueous ammonia to the solution of copper (II) ions. A pale blue precipitate is formed; this dissolves when more ammonia solution is added and a deep blue solution is formed.

Tests for common gases

a) **Hydrogen**
   If a test-tube of hydrogen is held to a flame, the impure hydrogen burns in air with a squeaky 'pop'

   $$2H_2(g) + O_2(g) \longrightarrow 2H_2O(l)$$

b) **Oxygen**
   If the glowing tip of a wooden splint is put into a test-tube of oxygen, the splint will burst into flame.

c) **Carbon dioxide**
   If carbon dioxide is bubbled through limewater (calcium hydroxide solution), a white precipitate of calcium carbonate forms initially and the solution appears cloudy or milky.

   $$Ca(OH)_2(aq) + CO_2(g) \longrightarrow CaCO_3(s) + H_2O(l)$$

   When excess carbon dioxide is then used, a colourless solution is formed which contains calcium hydrogencarbonate.

   $$CaCO_3(s) + H_2O(l) + CO_2(g) \longrightarrow Ca(HCO_3)_2(aq)$$

d) **Chlorine**   **POISONOUS**
   Chlorine is a yellow-green gas which can be recognised by its smell. It bleaches damp litmus paper and turns damp starch-iodide paper blue-black because of the formation of iodine.

   $$Cl_2 + 2I^- \longrightarrow 2Cl^- + I_2$$

e) **Sulphur dioxide**   **POISONOUS**
   Sulphur dioxide changes the colour of filter paper dipped into acidified potassium dichromate solution from orange to green.

f) **Ammonia**   **POISONOUS**
   Ammonia can be recognised by its smell; if the gas is tested with damp indicator paper, the indicator paper turns to the alkaline colour (blue with litmus or universal indicator). Ammonia is the only common alkaline gas.

   $$NH_3(aq) + H_2O(l) \rightleftharpoons NH_4^+(aq) + OH^-(aq)$$

Some old favourites

Diatomic Molecules

The magnificent 7 are:-

Hydrogen – H_2
Nitrogen – N_2
Oxygen – O_2
Fluorine – F_2
Chlorine – Cl_2
Bromine – Br_2
Iodine – I_2

General Equations

Metal	+ Oxygen	$\rightarrow$ Metal oxide			
e.g. 2Mg	+ O_2	$\rightarrow$ 2MgO			
Very reactive metal	+ Water	$\rightarrow$ Metal hydroxide	+ Hydrogen		
e.g. 2K	+ $2H_2O$	$\rightarrow$ 2KOH	+ H_2		
Reactive metal	+ Water	$\rightarrow$ Metal oxide	+ Hydrogen		
e.g. Mg	+ H_2O	$\rightarrow$ MgO	+ H_2		
Acid	+ Alkali	$\rightarrow$ Salt	+ Water		
e.g. HCl	+ NaOH	$\rightarrow$ NaCl	+ H_2O		
Acid	+ Metal	$\rightarrow$ Salt	+ Hydrogen		
e.g. 2HCl	+ Mg	$\rightarrow$ $MgCl_2$	+ H_2		
Carbonate	+ Acid	$\rightarrow$ Salt	+ Water	+ Carbon dioxide	
e.g. $CaCO_3$	+ 2HCl	$\rightarrow$ $CaCl_2$	+ H_2O	+ CO_2	
Hydrocarbon	+ Oxygen	$\rightarrow$ Carbon dioxide	+ Water		
e.g. CH_4	+ $2O_2$	$\rightarrow$ CO_2	+ $2H_2O$		

Equations and Quantities

$$moles = \frac{mass}{Mr}$$

$$concentration = \frac{moles}{volume}$$

I mole of any gas at room temperature and pressure has a volume of 24 litres.

The general formula for an alkane is C_nH_{2n+2}.

The general formula for an alkene is C_nH_{2n}.